Let's Visit Canada

Table of Contents

Written by Ruth Solski

Illustrated by Sean Parkes

ISBN - 0-921511-35-3

Let's Visit Canada

Learning Objectives

1. To have the students participate in a study of the country of Canada.
2. To introduce the concept of a map and a globe and to show how to use them to locate Canada.
3. To make students aware that Canada is divided into ten provinces and three territories.
4. To develop an awareness and recognition of the symbols that pertain to Canada.
5. To show students and to make them aware that Canadian customs and lifestyles vary across Canada.
6. To arouse a patriotic spirit in young Canadian students for their own country.
7. To show students that Canada is a mosaic of different cultures.

Vocabulary For Canada

The following vocabulary has been classified into various groups. Each group of words may be printed on an individual chart that bears the correct title, or the charts might bear headings to enable the students to brainstorm words that pertain to Canada. The teacher can classify the words on the correct charts.

The words on the charts may be numbered and a picture may be drawn beside each word, or a picture may be pasted beside it. Reproduce the picture cards in this unit and use them whenever you can on the vocabulary charts. This method enables students to locate (quickly and independently) words that they need to complete writing exercises and activities.

Many phonetic skills may be taught or reinforced using the charts.

e.g.
- Initial and Final Consonants
- Blends
- Digraphs
- Compound Words
- Syllabication
- Rhyming
- Long and Short Vowels
- Alphabetical Order

Canadian Words:

neighbourhood, community, country, province, territory, town, city, village, farm, ranch, lake, river, stream, mountains, waterfalls, flag, maple leaf, maple syrup, Canadian, French, English, multicultural, people, Prime Minister, Premier

Canadian Money:

cent, penny, nickel, dime, quarter, fifty cent piece, half dollar, one dollar coin (nicknamed the loonie), two dollar coin, paper money, coins

Let's Visit Canada

Grade 3

About This Book

Learn about Canada's land of towering mountains, lush green forests, fertile farmlands, northern wastelands and our mosaic of cultures with the 59 activities. Reproducible student booklet with answer key included.

Written by: Ruth Solski
Illustrated by: Sean Parkes
Item #J1-03

Original Publication: 1997
Revision: May 2003

Look For Other Canadian Units

Item #J1-01 Canada .... Gr. 1
J1-02 All About Canada 2
J1-03 Let's Visit Canada 3
J1-04 Canadian Provinces 3-6
J1-11 Wild Animals of Canada 2-3
J1-12 Famous Canadians 4-8
J1-13 Let's Look At Canada 4-6
J1-23 Ottawa 7-9
J1-32 What is Canada? .... P-K
J1-33 Canadian Capital Cities 4-6
J1-35 Toronto 4-8
J1-38 Canadian Provinces and Territories 4-6
J1-39 Canadian Government 5-8
J1-40 Development of Western Canada 7-8
J1-41 Canada and Its Trading Partners 6-8
J1-42 Canada's Traditions and Celebrations 1-3

Let's Visit...

J1-14 Let's Visit Saskatchewan 2-4
J1-15 Let's Visit British Columbia 2-4
J1-16 Let's Visit Alberta 2-4
J1-17 Let's Visit Ontario 2-4
J1-18 Let's Visit Manitoba 2-4
J1-19 Let's Visit Prince Edward Island 2-4
J1-20 Let's Visit Nova Scotia 2-4
J1-21 Let's Visit New Brunswick 2-4
J1-27 Let's Visit Newfoundland and Labrador 2-4
J1-28 Let's Visit Yukon Territory 2-4
J1-30 Let's Visit Northwest Territory 2-4
J1-31 Let's Visit Québec 2-4
J1-34 Let's Visit Nunavut 2-4

Discover Canada

J1-22 Discover Québec 5-7
J1-24 Discover Prince Edward Island 5-7
J1-25 Discover Ontario 5-7
J1-26 Discover Nova Scotia 5-7
J1-36 Discover Nunavut Territory 5-7

Canadian Communities

J1-05 Farming Community 3-4
J1-06 Fishing Community 3-4
J1-07 Mining Community 3-4
J1-08 Lumbering Community 3-4
J1-09 Ranching Community 3-4
J1-10 Inuit Community 3-4
J1-37 Canadian Arctic Inuit 2-3

Published by:
S&S Learning Materials
15 Dairy Avenue
Napanee, Ontario
K7R 1M4

Distributed in U.S.A. by:
T4T Learning Materials
5 Columba Drive, Suite 175
Niagara Falls, New York
14385

Let's Visit Canada

Canadian People:

French, English, Native People, Chinese, Japanese, West Indian, East Indian, Black, Pakistanian, Scottish, Irish, Korean, Viet Namese, Jamaican, Trinidadian, Spanish, German, Polish, Ukrainian, Russian, Swedish, Hungarian, Czechoslovakian, Italian, African, Inuit

Provinces and Territories:

Newfoundland, Nova Scotia, New Brunswick, Prince Edward Island, Québec, Ontario, Manitoba, Saskatchewan, Alberta, British Columbia, Yukon, Northwest Territories, Nunavut

Capital Cities:

St. John's (Newfoundland and Labrador); Halifax (Nova Scotia); Fredericton (New Brunswick); Charlottetown (Prince Edward Island); Québec City (Québec); Toronto (Ontario); Winnipeg (Manitoba); Regina (Saskatchewan); Edmonton (Alberta); Victoria (British Columbia); Yellowknife (Northwest Territories); Whitehorse (Yukon); Iqaluit (Nunavut); Ottawa (Canada)

Canadian Animals:

beaver, polar bear, black bear, grizzly bear, moose, deer, mountain goat, mountain sheep, wolf, chipmunk, fox, skunk, raccoon, woodchuck, porcupine, wolf, prairie dog, rabbit, caribou, musk ox, Arctic fox, Arctic wolf, opossum, lynx, mountain lion, weasel, brown bear, muskrat, seals, walrus, whales

Canadian Birds:

Canada goose, snowy owl, Arctic tern, bluejay, robin, crow, owl, chickadee, eagle, loon, duck, prairie grouse, crane, wren, sparrow, starling, heron, seagull, swan, hawk, gyrfalcon, hummingbird, junco, nuthatch

Canadian Fish:

salmon, trout, pike, pickerel, bass, herring, cod, mackeral, whitefish, halibut, flounder

Canadian Symbols:

flag, maple leaf, red colour, white colour, coat of arms, provincial flowers, provincial flags, provincial birds, provincial crests, beaver, moose, the Bluenose schooner, Bonhomme, polar bear, Royal Canadian Mounted Police (R.C.M.P.), maple syrup, Canadian money, Inuit art, totem poles

Canadian Sports:

hockey, baseball, football, soccer, basketball, volleyball, swimming, ice skating, tennis, golf, lacrosse, ringette, bowling, biking, kayaking, canoeing, hiking, sculling, skiing, gymnastics, curling

Let's Visit Canada

Famous Canadian Tourist and Historical Attractions:

Newfoundland and Labrador:

Cape Spear National Historic Park (St. John's); Captain James Cook Monument (Corner Brook); Castle Hill National Park (Placentia); Gros Morne National Park (Western Seacoast); Heart's Content Cable Station (Trinity Bay); L'Anse aux Meadows National Historic Site (tip of Great Northern Peninsula); Port au Choix National Historic Site (Great Northern Peninsula); Red Bay (Southern Coast of Labrador); Signal Hill National Historic Site and Cabot Tower (St. John's Harbour); Terra Nova National Park (Bonavista Bay); Trinity; Bell Island; Cape St. Mary's; Freshwater Resource Centre (St. John's); Grenfell House (St. Anthony); Marble Mountain Ski Area (Near Corner Brook); Port aux Basques Museum; the South Coast; Table Point Ecological Reserve (North of Gros Morne National Park); Wittondale Pioneer Village (Bonne Bay)

Prince Edward Island:

Ardgowan (Charlottetown); Basin Head Fisheries Museum (East of Souris); Beaconsfield (Charlottetown); Confederation Centre of the Arts (Charlottetown); Elmira Railway Museum (East of Souris); Eptek National Exhibition Centre (Summerside); Fort Amherst - Port La Joye National Historic Park (Near Charlottetown); Green Gables House (Cavendish); Green Park Shipbuilding Museum (Near Tyne Valley); Orwell Corner Historic Village (Near Charlottetown); Province House National Historic Site (Charlottetown); Acadian Museum of P.E.I. (Miscouche); Alberton Museum (Near Alberton); Dalton Centre (Tignish); Ellerslie Shellfish Museum (Bideford); Farmer's Bank Museum (South Rustico); Garden of the Gulf Museum (Montagne); International Fox Hall of Fame and Museum (Summerside); The Kier Memorial Museum (Malpeque Village); Lucy Maud Montgomery's Birthplace (New London); Micmac Indian Village (Rocky Point); Museum of Religious Art (Mont Carmel); Northumberland Mill and Museum (Near Murray River); O'Leary Centennial Museum (O'Leary); Veteran's Memorial Military Museum (Kensington); West Point Lighthouse Museum (Southwest tip of the Island)

New Brunswick:

Acadian Historical Village (Caraquet); Acadian Odyssey National Historic Site (Saint Joseph de Memramcock); Fort Beauséjour National Historic Site (Aulac); Kings Landing Historical Settlement (Fredericton); Kouchibouguac National Park (Acadian Coast); New Brunswick Legislative Assembly Building (Fredericton); New Brunswick Museum (Saint John); Beaverbrook Art Gallery (Fredericton); Grand Falls Gorge (Grand Falls); Hopewell Rocks (Hopewell Cape); Huntsman Marine Laboratory Museum and Aquarium (St. Andrews); Irving Nature Park (Saint John); Magnetic Hill (Moncton); Miramichi Atlantic Salmon Museum (Doaktown); Popes Museum (Grande - Anse); Sackville Waterfowl Park (Sackville)

Nova Scotia:

Fort Edward (Windsor); Grand Pré; Evangeline Statue; Fort Anne (Annapolis Royal); Port Royal (Annapolis Basin); Kejimkujik National Park (Southwestern Nova Scotia); Halifax Waterfront Buildings (Halifax); Bluenose II (Halifax); Halifax Citadel (Halifax); Louisbourg; Alexander Graham Bell National Historic Park at Baddeck (Cape Breton); St. Peter's Canal (St. Peter's);

Let's Visit Canada

Cape Breton Highlands National Park (Cape Breton); Cabot Trail (Cape Breton); Marconi National Historic Site (Glace Bay); Museum Headquarters (Halifax); Maritime Museum of the Atlantic (Halifax); Ross Farm Museum (New Ross); The Fisheries Museum of the Atlantic (Lunenburg); The Wile Carding Mill (Bridgewater); The Perkins House; The Ross-Thomson House (Shelburne); The Barrington Woolen Mill (Barrington); The Firefighters Museum (Yarmouth); North Hills Museum (Granville Ferry); The Haliburton House (Windsor); Uniake House (Mount Uniake); Lawrence House (Maitland); Balmoral Grist Mill (Tatamagouche); The Sutherland Steam Mill (Denmark); Fisherman's Life Museum (Jeddore - Oyster Pond); Sherbrooke Village (Sherbrooke); Cossit House (Sydney)

<u>Québec</u>:

Battle of Châteauguay National Historic Park (Châteauguay River); Château Montebello (Montebello); Cistercian Abbey (Oka); The Citadel (Québec City); Les Forges de Saint Maurice National Historic Park (Near Trois-Rivières); Fort Lennox National Historic Park (Ile-aux-Noix); The Fort Museum (Québec City); Lachine Canal (West of Museum); Laurier's House (Athabaska); The National Historic Park (Pointe-à-la-Croix); Native Museum of Pointe-Bleue (Pointe-Bleue); Patriots' Museum (Saint-Denis); Place d'Armes (Montréal); The walls of Quebéc (Québec);Basilica of Sainte-Anne-de-Beaupré (Beaupré); Bonaventure Island (Gulf of St. Lawrence); The Botannical Garden (Montréal); Cap-Tourmente National Wildlife Area (East of Beaupré); Fortillon National Park (Gaspé Peninsula); Gatineau Park (Laurentian Mountains); Iles-du-Bic (St.Lawrence near Rimouski); Les Jardins de Métis (Matane); Manic-Outarde Complex (Baie-Comeau); Matane Wildlife Reserve (Chic Choc Mountains); Montmorency Falls (Near Québec City); Olympic Park (Montréal); St. Joseph's Oratory (Montreal); Tadoussac (Mouth of Saguenay River); Wendake Indian Reserve (Near Québec City)

<u>Ontario</u>:

Casa Loma (Toronto); Gibson House (Toronto); Huron County Pioneer Museum (Goderich); Muskoka Pioneer Museum (Huntsville); Nancy Island Historic Site (Nancy Island, Wasaga Beach); Old Fort Erie (Fort Erie); Old Fort Henry (Kingston); Old Fort William (Near Thunder Bay); The Parliament Buildings (Ottawa); Sainte-Marie Among the Hurons (Midland); Upper Canada Village (Morrisburg); Amherstburg (Southern Ontario); Fort Malden; Bowmanville Museum (Bowmanville); Brantford; Joseph Brant Museum (Burlington); Black Creek Pioneer Village (Toronto); Canada's Wonderland (Toronto); Ontario Place (Toronto); Dundurn Castle (Hamilton); Elliot Lake Mining and Nuclear Museum (Elliot Lake); Martyr's Shrine (Midland); Moose Factory Island (Near Moosonee); CN Tower (Toronto); Parkwood (Oshawa); Pump House Steam Museum (Kingston); Serpent Mounds Provincial Park (Rice Lake); Niagara Falls; The Ukrainian and Cultural Museum (Timmins)

<u>Manitoba</u>:

Canada's National Ukrainian Festival Inc. (Dauphin); Dugald Costume Museum and Pioneer Home (Dugald); Eskimo Museum (Churchill); The Forks National Historic Site (Junction of the Red and Assiniboine Rivers); Fort Dauphin Museum (Dauphin); Fort la Reine Museum (Portage la Prairie); Grant's Old Mill (Winnipeg); Helca Village (East Side of Helca Island); Lower Fort

Garry National Historic Park (Fort Garry); Manitoba Agricultural Hall of Fame (Brandon); Manitoba Agricultural Museum (Austin); Manitoba Museum of Man and Nature (Winnipeg); Margaret Laurence House (Neepawa); Mennonite Heritage Village (Steinbach); Morden District Museum (Morden); Pembina Threshermen's Museum (Winkler); Prairie Dog Central Steam Train (Winnipeg); Riel House, National Historic Park (Winnipeg); Seven Oaks House (Winnipeg); St. Andrew's Church (On-the-Red) and St. Andrew's Rectory National Historic Park (North of Winnipeg); St. Boniface Basilica (St. Boniface); Western Canada Aviation Museum (International Airport); Assiniboine Park (Winnipeg); Clearwater Provincial Forestry Nursery (Northeast of The Pas); Delta Marsh (Northeast of Portage la Prairie); Fort Whyte Centre for Environmental Education; International Peace Garden (South of Boissevan); Souris; Souris Agate Pit (Souris)

Saskatchewan:

Batouche National Historic Park (Batouche); Battleford National Historic Park (Battleford); Cannington Manor Historic Park (Southeast Moose Mountain); Cumberland House Historic Park (Cumberland House); Fort Pitt Provincial Historic Park; Fort Walsh National Historic Park (Cypress Hills); Government House Historic Property (Regina); Last Mountain House Provincial Historic Park (Near Craven); Motherwell Homestead National Historic Park (Abernethy); St. Victor's Petroglyphs Provincial Historic Park; Stanley Mission Provincial Historic Site (North of La Ronge); Wood Mountain Post Provincial Historic Park (Close to the U.S. Border); Allen Sapp Galley (North Battleford); John G. Diefenbaker Centre (University of Saskatchewan); The Legislative Building (Regina); Manitou Beach; National Doukhobour Heritage Village (Veregin); Pelican Narrows (Northwest of Flin Flon); Prince Albert National Park; R.C.M.P. Centennial Museum and Chapel (Regina); Saskatchewan Museum of Natural History (Regina); Wanuskewin Heritage Park (North of Saskatoon)

Alberta:

Mormon Church (Cardston); Head-Smashed-In Buffalo Jump; Twelve-Foot Davis' Grave (Peace River); Banff Springs Hotel; Heritage Park (Calgary); Legislative Buildings (Edmonton); Fort Macleod; Fort Calgary (Calgary); John Ware's Cabin (Near Dinosaur Provincial Park); Fort Whoop-up; Stephan Stephanson's Home (Near Red Deer); George Burnet Farm (Rich Valley); Hoodoos (The Badlands); Columbia Ice Fields (Between Banff and Jasper); Frank Slide (Turtle Mountain); Oil Sands (Fort McMurray); Rocky Mountains; West Edmonton Mall (Edmonton); Calaway Park (Calgary); Spruce Meadows (Calgary); Jasper; Banff; Lake Louise; Lesser Slave Lake; Japanese Gardens (Lethbridge); Royal Tyrrell Museum (Drumheller); Giant Pysanka (Vegreville); Calgary Stampede (Calgary)

British Columbia:

Barkerville Historic Park (Barkerville); Doukhobour Heritage Village (Castlegar); Fort Langley National Historic Site (Fort Langley); Fort Steele (Near Cranbrook); Fort St. James National Historic Park (Fort St. James); Provincial Legislative Buildings (Victoria); West Coast Trail (Southwestern Coast of Vancouver Island); Botanical Beach (West Coast of Vancouver Island); Chinatown (Vancouver); Fisgard Lighthouse National Historic Site (Esquimmalt Harbour); Ninstints (Anthony Island); O'Keefe Historic Ranch (Okanagan Valley); Sasquatch Provincial Park (Harrison Lake); Stanley Park (Vancouver); Grouse Mountain

(Vancouver); Butchart Gardens (Victoria); Capilano Suspension Bridge (Vancouver); Totem Poles (various places); Ksan Village (near Churchill)

The Yukon:

Canol Road (Connects Norman Wells, N.W.T. to Whitehorse, Yukon); Herschel Island (Coast of the Yukon); S.S. Klondike (Whitehorse); Robert Service Cabin (Dawson City); Jack London's Cabin and Interpretive Centre (Dawson City); Fort Selkirk; The Chilkoot Trail; Coal River Hot Springs; Ivvavik National Park; Takhini Hot Springs (Near Whitehorse)

Northwest Territories:

Inukshuk (Stone Markers); Inuvik; Whitehorse; Nahanni National Park (Western Mainland); Aulavik Park on Banks Island; Waterfalls Route Along the Mackenzie Highway; Prince of Wales Northern Heritage Centre

Nunavut:

Auyuittuq National Park (Baffin Island); Ellesmere Island National Park; North Baffin National Park; Keberten Historic Park (Near Pangnirtung); Quaummaarviit Historic Park (Near Iqaluit); Katannilik Territorial Park (Baffin Island);Beechey Island; Bathurst Inlet Lodge; Sila Lodge (Wager Bay); Angmarlik Visitors Centre (Pangnirtung); Northwest Passage Historic Park (Gjoa Haven); Tunooniq Theatre (Pond Inlet); Coman Arctic Gallery (Iqaluit); West Baffin Eskimo Co-operative (Cape Dorset); Baker Lake Inuit Camp (Baker Lake)

Provincial Trivia

Newfoundland and Labrador:

Bird: Puffin; **Flower**: Pitcher Plant; **Tree**: Black Spruce; **Nickname**: "The Rock"

Prince Edward Island:

Bird: Bluejay; **Flower**: Lady's Slipper; **Tree**: Northern Red Oak; **Song**: The Island Hymn (Written by L.M. Montgomery); **Nicknames**: "Spud Island", "Million Acre Farm", "The Garden Province", "Abegweit", "Minegoo", "The Island"

New Brunswick:

Bird: Black-Capped Chickadee; **Flower**: Purple Violet; **Tree**: Balsam Fir; **Nickname**: "Picture Province"

Nova Scotia:

Bird: No Provincial Bird; **Flower**: Mayflower; **Tree**: Red Spruce; **Nicknames**: "Land of Evangeline", "Canada's Ocean Playground"; **Song**: "Farewell to Nova Scotia"

Québec:

Bird: Snowy Owl; **Flower**: Madonna Lily; **Nickname**: "La Belle Province"

Let's Visit Canada

<u>Ontario</u>:

<u>Bird</u>: Common Loon; **<u>Flower</u>**: White Trillium; **<u>Tree</u>**: Eastern White Pine

<u>Manitoba</u>:

<u>Bird</u>: Great Gray Owl; **<u>Flower</u>**: Prairie Crocus; **<u>Nickname</u>**: "Keystone Province"

<u>Saskatchewan</u>:

<u>Bird</u>: Prairie Sharp-Tailed Grouse; **<u>Flower</u>**: Western Red Lily; **<u>Nickname</u>**: "The Wheat Province"; **<u>Tree</u>**: White Birch

<u>Alberta</u>:

<u>Bird</u>: Great Horned Owl; **<u>Flower</u>**: Wild Rose; **<u>Tree</u>**: Lodgepole Pine; **<u>Nicknames</u>**: "Princess Province", "Energy Province"

<u>British Columbia</u>:

<u>Bird</u>: Stellar Jay; **<u>Flower</u>**: Pacific Dogwood; **<u>Tree</u>**: Western Red Cedar; **<u>Nickname</u>**: "The Pacific Province"

<u>The Yukon</u>:

<u>Bird</u>: Raven; **<u>Flower</u>**: Fireweed; **<u>Nickname</u>**: "Land of the Midnight Sun"

<u>Northwest Territories</u>:

<u>Bird</u>: Gyrfalcon; **<u>Flower</u>**: Mountains Avens; **<u>Tree</u>**: Jack Pine; **<u>Nicknames</u>**: "Canada's Last Frontier", "Land of the Polar Bear", "North of Sixty"

<u>Nunavut</u>:

At this present time, this territory has not selected symbols that will represent it.

Teacher Information

Canada

Introduction:

Canada is the second largest country in the world. It is found in the continent of North America. Canada stretches from Newfoundland on the Atlantic coast to British Columbia on the Pacific coast. The United States is Canada's neighbour to the south. Canada is slightly larger than the United States in area but the United States has a much larger population. More than 28 million people live in Canada and 75 percent live within 150 kilometres (100 miles) of the southern border. The northern part of Canada is uninhabited or thinly populated because the country has a rugged terrain and a severe climate.

Canada is a diverse land. The western coastal areas are quite beautiful with towering mountains, crystal clear lakes and lush forests. The prairies are covered with fields of wheat and other grains. In the far Arctic northlands, large areas are barren or covered with snow. Canada's largest population and manufacturing centres are

Let's Visit Canada

located near the Great Lakes and the St. Lawrence River in Central Canada. Fishing villages and sandy beaches dot the country's Atlantic coast.

Important Facts:

- Capital of Canada - Ottawa
- Official Languages - English and French
- Size (Area) - 9 970 610 km^2 (3 849 674 sq.mi.)
- Population - 28 537 000 (Estimated population 1996)
- National Anthem - "O Canada"
- National Symbols - maple leaf, beaver
- National Holidays - Canada Day, July 1
- Money - Basic Unit - dollar
- Leader - Prime Minister

Regions of Canada

Canada is a federation (union) of ten provinces and three territories. The country's name probably comes from "Kanata - Kon", an Iroquois native word that means *to the village* or *to the small houses.*

Canada has six cultural and economic regions. They are:

- The Atlantic Provinces
- Québec
- Ontario
- The Prairie Provinces
- British Columbia
- The Territories

The **Atlantic Provinces** lie on the Atlantic Ocean. The four provinces are Newfoundland, New Brunswick, Prince Edward Island and Nova Scotia. They make up five percent of Canada's land area, and nine percent of the people live here.

The Atlantic Provinces have been an important fishing centre for hundreds of years. These provinces provide Canada with different types of seafood, although only three percent of the people are employed in the fishing industry. The main industry is manufacturing. Agriculture, mining, shipping and tourism are also important.

The Atlantic Provinces have suffered many economic difficulties in the past. This region has a lower standard of living, lower wages and a higher rate of unemployment than any other part of Canada. At the present time fishers are not allowed to fish for cod.

Québec is quite different from the rest of Canada because of its French Language and culture. French is the official language of Québec and most of the people living there belong to the Roman Catholic Church. Québec is the largest province in area and the second largest in population. Montréal is the largest city in Québec and it is the centre of the province's economic and cultural life. It is also Canada's leading transportation centre. Manufacturing and service industries such as banks, hospitals and advertising agencies are the largest industries. People also work in agriculture, mining, forestry and fishing.

Let's Visit Canada

Ontario has the largest population of all the provinces. More than one third of Canada's people live here. Ontario's southern boundary passes through four of the five Great Lakes which are Superior, Huron, Erie and Ontario. The province's main manufacturing area is sometimes called the "Golden Horseshoe". It lies on the western shore of Lake Ontario and includes Toronto, Hamilton and St. Catharines. Ontario makes more than half of Canada's manufactured goods and is also the leading agricultural province. Toronto is Ontario's capital city and is also the largest city in Ontario. It is a very important manufacturing, financial, cultural and communications centre in English-speaking Canada.

The **Prairie Provinces** are Alberta, Saskatchewan and Manitoba. The southern part of this region has many wheat farms and cattle ranches while the northern area contains numerous lakes and forests. For many years this area was isolated from eastern Canada until the first transcontinental railroad in 1885 made it easy to reach this region. In the late 1800's and the early 1900's, hundreds of thousands of people settled on the fertile Canadian prairies. The many settlers came from eastern Canada, the United States, Germany, Italy, the Netherlands, Poland, the Ukraine, Denmark, Norway and Sweden. Agriculture, petroleum and natural gas are the Prairie Provinces' main resources. Edmonton, Regina and Winnipeg are the capital cities and they also are the largest.

British Columbia is Canada's third largest province in area and population. It is located on the west coast of Canada. British Columbia's natural beauty, rugged coastline and lofty mountains attract many tourists.

Victoria is the capital city and is located on Vancouver Island. Vancouver is the province's largest city and has the busiest port in Canada. Southern British Columbia has the mildest climate in Canada and many older Canadians move here to retire.

Half of the population in British Columbia have English ancestry while others are from Scottish, Irish and German descent. Of all the provinces British Columbia has the highest percentage of Asians.

Logging and wood-processing industries provide work for most of the people. Other economic activities include agriculture, fishing and mining.

The **Territories** are known as the Yukon Territory, the Northwest Territories and Nunavut. Nunavut became an official territory in 1999. These territories make up more than a third of Canada's land area. They are located in a remote location and have a severe climate. Only one per cent of Canada's people live in the territories. The land consists mainly of forest-covered mountains or is a frozen wasteland. The territories have rich mineral deposits and mining is the main economic activity.

Mainly Inuit and Native People made their homes here until great mineral wealth was discovered during the late 1800's and early 1900's. The capital city of the Yukon Territory is called Whitehorse. It was founded during the Klondike Gold Rush of the late 1890's. Yellowknife, the capital of the Northwest Territories, was built during another gold rush in the 1930's. The capital city for Nunavut is Iqaluit. This territory was carved out of the Northwest Territories.

Let's Visit Canada

Canada's People

Canada has an estimated population of 28 537 000 (1996). Almost all Canadians are of European descent. Two per cent of Canada's people are Native People and Inuit. Forty-five per cent have some British ancestry which includes English, Irish, Scottish and Welsh descent. Thirty-one per cent have some French ancestry. Other large ethnic groups include Germans and Italians.

Native People and Inuit were living on this land for thousands of years before the Europeans first arrived. Today, there are nearly 550 000 Native People and about 36 000 Inuit living in Canada. The word *Inuit* means "people". They were once called Eskimos, an American word, meaning "eaters of raw meat". The Inuit live in the Northwest Territories, Nunavut and the northern areas of Newfoundland, Ontario and Québec. Canada's Native People belong to one of ten major groups - the Algonquian, the Athapaskan, the Haida, the Iroquoian, the Kootenayan, the Salishan, the Siouan, the Tlingit, the Tsimshian and the Wakashan. Most Native people in Canada live on more than 2 200 reserves (reservations).

Other Canadians include people from China, India and Pakistan and other Asians. These people make up about nine per cent of the population of British Columbia. Many immigrants such as people from China, the Indian subcontinent and the West Indies have settled in Toronto. One percent of Canada's population is Black. Many Black Canadians are of West Indian descent and come from English-speaking islands and French-speaking Haiti.

Canadian Languages

Canada has two official languages - English and French. Sixty-nine per cent of the Canadian people speak mainly English in the home. Twenty-four per cent speak mainly French. Six per cent of the Canadian people speak other languages such as Italian, Chinese, German, Portuguese etc.

Most of Canada's French-speaking citizens live in Québec. French-speaking Canadians are called Québecois (kay beh KWAH) and consider themselves the guardians of the French language and culture in Canada. In 1974, the Québec government adopted French as Québec's official language. This act meant that French was to be promoted in schools and it was the official language of business and government. All outdoor signs, traffic signs and advertisements must be written in French.

Canadian Lifestyles

In Canada today, seventy-seven per cent of the people live in cities or urban areas. The cities are filled with skyscrapers, subway systems and expressway systems to link the cities with the suburbs. Toronto and Montréal have modern subway systems. Canada has twenty-seven metropolitan areas with a population of more than 100 000. The three largest metropolitan areas are Montréal, Qué; Toronto, Ont. and Vancouver, B.C.. Other major Canadian metropolitan areas are Ottawa, Ont; Hull, Qué; Calgary, Alta; Edmonton, Alta; Hamilton, Ont; Québec City, Qué. and Winnipeg, Man.

Let's Visit Canada

People who live in Canadian cities have many opportunites and activities in which to participate. They can attend plays, concerts, and sporting events or visit parks and museums.

Many of Canada's smaller cities are relatively quiet, safe and pleasant to live in. Some of the larger cities have experienced social problems, and reductions in transportation and welfare funds. Racial tension among ethnic groups has appeared with the immigration to the cities by various people from many nations. Many Canadians are disturbed by the disappearance of valuable farmland through suburban expansion.

Twenty-three per cent of Canada's people live in the country or rural areas. Only four per cent live on farms. Many Canadians live in rural communities and commute to their jobs every day. Some Canadians work at industries such as fishing, mining and lumbering.

Canadian farmers usually own their own farms and farming is a family affair. The farms are worked with modern machinery and technology. Canada's largest farms are found in the Prairie Provinces. They are usually 435 hectares (1 075 acres) in size. Farms in Ontario, Québec and the Atlantic Provinces are much smaller and average about 73 to 120 hectares (180 to 300 acres).

Most of Canada's farmland is found in the Prairie Provinces. The golden prairies are dotted with wooden farmhouses, buildings to store machinery and grain, and large grain elevators.

Life in Canada's vast Arctic region is quite different from life in the rest of the country. The region is very thinly populated. The Inuit and Native People have been its main occupants for thousands of years. They form forty percent of the region's population. Other people are traders, miners, and members of the armed forces and the Royal Canadian Mounted Police.

Some of the Inuit still practise their traditional ways of life such as fishing, hunting and trapping. In many ways, however, the old ways of life in the Arctic have ended. The people live in modern houses rather than in tents or igloos. They wear modern clothing, eat food bought in stores and travel with snowmobiles, terrain vehicles and motorboats instead of dog sleds and kayaks.

Canadian Food

Canadians enjoy eating many different types of food. The abundance of food grown in Canada and its accessibility has made many children and adults overweight and obese. Canadians enjoy eating many local specialities such as Eastern Clam Chowder, Habitant Pea Soup, Buffalo Birds, Tourtière (Québec Pork Pie), Onion Soup with Cheese, Ratatouille (onions, peppers, tomatoes), French Bread, Maple Syrup, Smoked Fish, Potato Soup and Maritime Baked Beans.

Let's Visit Canada

The many immigrants who made their homes in Canada have given Canadian food a cosmopolitan flavour. Canadians enjoy dining at various eating establishments such as Japanese, Chinese, Caribbean, Italian, Indian, Ukrainian and Asian restaurants. They also enjoy eating at many fast food outlets where hamburgers, French fries, hotdogs, tacos, and deep fried chicken is sold.

Canadian Schools

Early schools in Canada were operated by various religious groups. In 1867, the British North American Act made education the responsibility of the provincial governments. Each province and territory has its own school system. Each school system is supervised by the provincial or territorial department of education. A cabinet minister heads each department and reports to the province's government. The education for children on Native reserves, members of the armed forces and immates of federal penitentiaries is directed by the Canadian government.

In most provinces, school systems have twelve grades. Québec's system has eleven grades and Ontario is currently changing from thirteen to twelve grades. In most provinces there is a public school system and a separate school system. In Québec, the school system consists of separate schools for Roman Catholics and Protestants. In Catholic schools the students are taught in French and in Protestant schools the students are taught in English. All immigrant children in Québec must attend schools that teach French. In Newfoundland, children may choose to attend schools run by the Pentecostals, Roman Catholics, Seventh-Day Adventists or Protestants.

Canada has many important colleges and universities. In some of the universities the classes are taught in French, but the majority of the universities teach in English. The major English-Language universities include the University of Alberta, the University of British Columbia, the University of Toronto, the University of Western Ontario, York University, McGill University, Concordia University and Bishop's University. Important French language universities are the University of Moncton, the University of Ste.-Anne and various universities in Québec. The University of Ottawa is a bilingual university.

Canada's Religions

The Roman Catholic faith is the largest religious group in Canada. Most other Canadians are Protestants. Protestant churches are Anglican, Presbyterian, Lutheran or Baptist. Other religious groups are Jewish, Muslims, Buddhists, Hindus and Sikhs.

Canadian Recreation and Sports

Canada's climate provides a wide variety of seasonal recreational activities and sports. In the winter many people enjoy skiing, snowshoeing, skating and tobogganing. Popular summer sports include swimming, canoeing, fishing, hiking, tennis and golf.

Canada's first national game was Lacrosse which the Native People played before the Europeans came to North America. Hockey is considered the most popular sport in Canada. Many famous hockey players such as Wayne Gretzky, Gordie Howe, Guy Lafleur and Bobby Orr have become national heroes in Canada.

Let's Visit Canada

Other professional and amateur sports in Canada include football, basketball, baseball and soccer.

Work of the Canadian People

The people of Canada work at a variety of jobs. Most of the people work in industries that provide services for Canadians. They may be teachers, doctors, nurses, police officers, store clerks, etc.

Many people work in factories where they make things that people need and buy in Canada. These factories produce cars and trucks, process meat and poultry, make food products, create paper products and manufacture many more items.

In some areas where large deposits of minerals have been found, Canadians work in mines. They may extract minerals such as copper, gold, iron ore, nickel, potash, uranium and zinc.

Canada has good farmland in most of its provinces and many Canadians make their living by farming. In Canada, dairy farms, mixed farms and cattle ranches are found in various provinces. Many products are grown and raised on these farms such as cattle, poultry, wheat, hogs, corn, other grains, fruits, vegetables and many more things.

Large forests of evergreen trees and deciduous trees are found throughout Canada. Some Canadians work in the logging industry. They are loggers and they cut down trees that are sent to mills to turn the logs into lumber, paper, plywood and wood pulp.

On the coasts of Canada, fishing is a way of life. It is Canada's oldest industry. Fishing crews provide Canadians with products such as cod, lobster, crab, scallops, salmon, herring and halibut. At the present time there is a moritorium on fishing cod in the Atlantic Ocean that borders the Atlantic Provinces.

Bibliography of Canadian Resources

Kalman, Bobbie. **Canada Celebrates Multiculturalism**. Crabtree Publishing Company; © 1993

Kalman, Bobbie. **Canada, the Land**. Crabtree Publishing Company; © 1993

Kalman, Bobbie. **Canada, the People**. Crabtree Publishing Company; © 1993

Kalman, Bobbie. **Canada, the Culture**. Crabtree Publishing Company; © 1993

Kelly, Lisa. **Shawn and Jessica's Great Canadian Adventure Series**. Primary People's Press; 3-251 Queen Street South, Suite 531, Mississauga, Ontario, Canada, L5M 1L7; © 1994

This series has individual books written on each province and territory.

- Welcome to Prince Edward Island
- Welcome to Saskatchewan
- Welcome to Alberta
- Welcome to British Columbia
- Welcome to The Yukon
- Welcome to the Northwest Territories
- Welcome to Manitoba
- Welcome to Newfoundland
- Welcome to Nova Scotia
- Welcome to New Brunswick
- Welcome to Québec
- Welcome to Ontario

Let's Visit Canada

Harrison, Ted. **O Canada**. Kids Can Press; © 1992

Lerner Publications Company. **Hello Canada** Series.

- Prince Edward Island
- Nova Scotia
- New Brunswick
- Québec
- Newfoundland and Labrador
- Alberta
- British Columbia
- Yukon
- Northwest Territories
- Saskatchewan
- Manitoba
- Nunavut
- Ontario

Teacher Input Suggestions

Planning Ahead:

Well in advance of completing this unit in your classroom begin to collect as many of the following items as possible:

- Fiction and nonfiction books that pertain to Canada
- Photographs and pictures of famous places found in Canada
- Pictures of famous Canadians and symbols of Canada
- Crests and flags that represent the ten provinces and the three territories
- Pictures of the provincial and territorial floral emblems and birds
- A large Canadian flag
- A picture of the present Prime Minister of Canada
- Pictures of Canadian animals
- Pictures of the different types of Canadian people that make Canada a mosaic country
- Maps of Canada and the individual provinces, road maps, atlases, large flat maps, globes
- A puzzle map of Canada
- Canadian postcards
- Canadian Travel Brochures and Pamphlets
- Samples of foods that are made in Canada
- Films, filmstrips, videos and slides that pertain to Canada

Let's Visit Canada

Bulletin Board Displays:

Use any of the suggested ideas to make a display on your bulletin board.

1. **What is Canada?**

   On the bulletin board place a large map of Canada. Connect string or wool to each province. At the end of each piece of string attach a card bearing the name of each province.

   This same display could be done on the chalkboard. Glue magnetic tape to the back of the map and to the back of provincial and territorial name cards. Use this display as part of a Mapping Centre. The children will use the name cards to place on the correct province. Have a sample map with the names of the provinces and territories on it for the students to use as a reference. Entitle the display "What is Canada?"

2. **Canada's Symbols:**

   On a bulletin board, display a map of Canada. Around the map display pictures of items or three dimensional objects that represent Canada such as a small Canadian Flag, a maple leaf, a beaver, the Royal Canadian Mounted Police, Canadian money, a picture of the Prime Minister and the Parliament Buildings (Ottawa), Canada's Coat of Arms, a polar bear, the Bluenose Schooner, maple syrup and totem poles. Label each symbol with a name card. Entitle the display "Symbols of Canada".

3. **Canadian Communities:**

   On a bulletin board display a large map of Canada. Around the map place pictures of different types of Canadian communities such as fishing, farming, mining, manufacturing, lumbering, ranching and Inuit. Connect the various communities to the areas in Canada where they are located. Entitle the display "Canadian Communities".

4. **We Are Canadians:**

   On a large bulletin board display a large flag of Canada. Around the flag display pictures of different families or people who are Canadians such as Caucasion, Black, Native Canadians, Inuit, Asians, Pakistanian, Sikhs, etc. Entitle the display "We Are Proud Canadians".

5. **Tourist Attractions:**

   On a bulletin board display and label famous tourist attractions. Entitle the display "Famous Places to Visit in Canada".

6. **Animals of Canada:**

   Display pictures of Canadian Animals such as the beaver, polar bear, bald eagle, snowy owl, black squirrel, grizzly bear, seal, Arctic Fox, lemming, muskrat, Canada Goose, mountain sheep, moose, deer, caribou, raccoon and porcupine. Make up rhymes or riddles about each one. Print them on cards. Read the riddles or rhymes to your students or have them read the riddles or rhymes and then have them match the rhyme or riddle to each picture. Entitle the display "We Live in Canada Too".

Let's Visit Canada

7. **Famous People:**

   To familiarize students with famous Canadians, display pictures of these people on a bulletin board. Label each one. Discuss the importance of each famous Canadian. Entitle the display "We Are Famous Canadians".

8. On a chart print the words to Canada's National Anthem called "O Canada". Display the anthem on a bulletin board. Around the anthem display Canadian symbols and pictures of well known Canadian places or buildings. Use the chart to practise saying the words and singing them everyday.

   Use the chart to teach or review the following phonetic skills.

   - Locate all the words that have blends. e.g. pat**r**iot, **gl**owing, **tr**ue, **str**ong, **fr**ee, **st**and, **gl**orious, **fr**om
   - Locate all the words that have digraphs. e.g. **th**y, **th**ee, Nor**th**
   - Locate the long a words. e.g. **native, patriot**
   - Locate all the long e words. e.g. **thee, free, we, keep**
   - Locate all the long o words. e.g. **home, glowing, glorious, North**
   - Locate all the short o words. e.g. **patriot, love, sons, strong, God, command**
   - Locate three syllable words. e.g. **Canada, glorious, patriot**
   - Locate two syllable words. e.g. **native, command, glowing**

   Explain to your students the meaning of some of the lines and difficult words such as "native land", "patriot love", "glowing hearts", "glorious", "command".

   Teach your class to sing the anthem correctly in English and if you think your students can handle the French version, teach it as well. Use the reproducible song sheets provided in the unit while learning to sing or read the anthem. The students may finger point in a rhythmical manner while they do this activity. The teacher may be doing the same exercise on an overhead or chart so the children can view the rhythm pattern. The students may also underline, box, circle, cross out, colour with certain colours the words that you want to reinforce or test.

Canada's National Anthem

(English Version)

O Canada

O Canada! Our home and native land!

True patriot love in all thy sons command

With glowing hearts we see thee rise,

The true North strong and free!

From far and wide, O Canada,

We stand on guard for thee.

God keep our land glorious and free!

O Canada, we stand on guard for thee.

O Canada, we stand on guard for thee.

Canada's National Anthem

(French Version)

Ô Canada

Ô Canada, terre de nos aïeux

Ton front est ceint de fleurons glorieux

Car ton bras sait porter l'épée

Il sait porter la croix;

Ton histoire est une épopée

Des plus brillants exploits

Et ta valeur, de foi trempée

Protégera nos foyers et nos droits

Protégera nos foyers et nos droits

Let's Visit Canada

Introductions:

Use any of the following suggestions:

1. Play Canada's National Anthem without any words to see if the students recognize the tune. Then listen to a version that does have the vocal. Have your students sing along if they can. Play the National Anthem every day and have the students participate. It is **extremely** important that Canadian children know how to sing their own National Anthem.
2. Show a video, film or filmstrip on Canada and discuss the various places seen in the film. List their names on a chart. Put a checkmark beside any places the students have visited in Canada. This could become a graphing exercise.
3. Read Ted Harrison's "O Canada" to the students and discuss the pictures of the various places. Discuss the way in which the artist depicted the places and the colours he used.
4. Establish an Interest Centre entitled "Let's Look at Canada". At the centre, place Canadian souvenirs, postcards, books, dolls, foods, pictures, etc. Discuss the centre and have the students add things to it as the unit proceeds. During discussion time the students may talk about the items that they are contributing to the centre and tell where they came from in Canada. Make sure that you send a letter home to the parents of your students informing them of the topic and ask them so assist their children in locating Canadian items.

Discussion Topics:

Discuss any of the following topics with your students. Try to make a chart story after each discussion.

a) Location of Canada on a wall map and a globe
b) The concept of a village, town, city, province or territory, country
c) Size of Canada in comparison to other countries (use a map or globe)
d) People who live in Canada - emphasize the multicultural mosaic
e) The Canadian Flag - colours; maple leaf; meaning of colours; importance of maple leaf
f) Canadian Symbols - maple leaf, Royal Canadian Mounted Police, beaver, polar bear, Bluenose Schooner, Bonhomme, Canada Goose, money
g) Landforms in Canada - rivers, lakes, waterfalls, mountains, hills, oceans, bays, islands, etc. (Refer to a wall map or use pictures of the various landforms.)
h) Climate in Canada - four definite seasons: winter, spring, summer, fall; very cold in northern areas; some areas get snow while others receive a great deal of rain.
I) Canadian Animals - moose, black bear, grizzly bear, polar bear, deer, beaver, raccoon, skunk, lemming, fox, etc.
j) Canadian Sports - hockey, lacrosse, baseball, basketball, track and field, swimming, etc.
k) Ottawa - Canada's Capital City; home of the Prime Minister; Parliament Buildings
l) Products grown in Canada - wheat, apples, etc.
m) A brief outline of Canada's history
n) The importance of Canada and why we should be proud of it

Let's Visit Canada

Art Ideas

At an art centre have the students participate in any of the following art activities. Make sure that you provide the students with the necessary supplies at the centre.

1. **Canadian Scenes:**

   Use a shoebox or any small box to make a diorama. Have the students decorate the

   sides and back of the box with scenery on the inside. People and objects may be modelled out of modelling clay and placed in the diorama.

2. **Painting:**

   Students may paint individual scenes of famous tourist attractions that they have visited.

3. **Canadian Flags:**

   The students may illustrate and colour the various provincial flags, attach them to sticks and put them on display.

4. **Canadian Souvenirs**:

   The students may design and create Canadian postcards, Canadian greeting cards, Canadian book marks, Canadian banners, hats and t-shirts.

5. **Paper Bag Puppets or Stick Puppets**:

   Paper bag or stick puppets may be made for Canadian animals, Canadian people or Canadian settlers. They may be used for puppet plays, story telling or poetry recitations.

Music:

Teach songs about Canada during your vocal music programme. There are some excellent songs and poems in a student songbook entitled "Canada is..... Music", published by Gordon V. Thompson Limited, Toronto, Canada.

At a listening centre the students may listen to music sung or played by famous Canadian music artists such as Anne Murray, Stomping Tom Connors, Gordon Lightfoot, Buffy Ste Marie, Raffi etc.

Literature:

Read a variety of poems about Canada e.g. "In Kamloops" by Dennis Lee. Collect a variety of native legends and Canadian legends and share them with your class. Share a variety of stories written by famous Canadian authors.

Canadian Scrapbooks:

At an interest centre place a variety of labelled scrapbooks and various Canadian Magazines. Each scrapbook should bear a title. Choose titles from the list below.

- Famous Canadians
- Capital Cities

Let's Visit Canada

- Famous Canadian Scenes or Tourist Attractions
- People of Canada
- Animals of Canada
- Transportation in Canada
- Canadian Workers
- Canadian Children
- Canadian Birds
- Canadian Water Animals
- Canadian Homes
- Canadian Recipes
- Individual Provinces
- Postcards

The student may choose a picture, cut it out neatly and glue it in the correct scrapbook. The student may write a few sentences about the picture.

Mapping Centre:

At a mapping centre, place any of the following items:

- a puzzle map of Canada for the students to assemble
- globes, road maps and atlases for the students to explore
- outline maps of Canada for the students to label and colour
- outline maps of the provinces for the students to trace and label

Interest Centre:

Establish a Canada Interest Centre. At the centre display pictures, souvenirs, maps, books, postcards, travel magazines, posters, and travel brochures. Encourage your students to add Canadian souvenirs, photos, etc. that they have collected.

Mathematics:

1. Review the concept of Canadian currency. Discuss its appearance, shape, colour, illustrations and value. Have the students practise paying for items and making change.
2. Discuss large numerals especially when referring to populations of provinces and cities. Review place value, sequencing numerals, collecting numerals, and reading and writing numeral words over 1000.

Miscellaneous Ideas:

1. Plan to take your class on an excursion to a local tourist attraction.
2. Invite a local politician to your classroom to talk about the importance of his/her community to the rest of Canada. He/She could discuss the aspects of being a patriotic citizen and the importance of showing patriotism to Canada.
3. Celebrate Flag Day which takes place on February 15th with a birthday party. Serve a big flag cake and icecream. Have the students go outside and salute the flag and sing "Happy Birthday" and "O Canada". Discuss the importance of Canada's flag.

4. Watch videos and movies that show Canada in early settler days and ones that show Canada as it is today.
5. Have a "Canada Day" or "Heritage Day" celebration to conclude the unit on Canada. Encourage students from ethnic backgrounds to wear their traditional costumes and have them discuss them with their classmates. Perhaps a variety of ethnic foods may be brought from home and served at a "Multicultural Luncheon"
6. Try to locate old basal readers or anthologies that have Canadian Stories. Design activities that may be used with the stories for the children to complete.

Reproducible Student Booklet

The student booklet may be used in the following ways.

1. Use the booklet as a teacher directed tool, as an introduction to Canada or as a follow-up to end the unit. Each page may be used as a follow-up to a class discussion or as a review to test the students' ability to absorb information. The students fill in the missing words with the aid of the classroom teacher. An answer key for the booklet has been provided at the back of the unit.
2. The booklet may be reproduced and colated and sent home for parents and students to work at as a homework assignment.
3. The booklet may be used as a research tool. The children may work in the resource centre with the teacher-librarian to locate answers.
4. Individual pages may be placed at a reading centre for the students to complete independently.
5. Make overheads of the pages and use them for large group reading activities.

Independent Activity Centre Ideas

Note: Independent Activity centres should not be used until the students have been introduced well to the information pertaining to the theme. Teacher input is essential through the use of visual aids, group discussions, guest speakers or class excursions.

Activity Preparation:

1. In the unit, activities for the following centres have been developed.

- Maxine Maple Leaf's Sounds
- Louie Lumberjack's Word Study
- Bonhomme's Brainstorming
- Fiona Fisher's Map Reading
- Cochrane Cowboy's Research
- Maggie Miner's Printing/Writing
- Farmer Fraser's Creative Writing
- Constable Mackenzie's Reading
- Iona Inuit's Mathematics

Let's Visit Canada

2. Some of the activities are to be used as manipulatives. They should be cut out, coloured, mounted on a sturdy backing and laminated. The pieces should be stored in an envelope that has the instruction card attached. Each manipulative activity has an accompanying instruction card. The instruction card should be cut out, coloured, mounted on a sturdy backing and then laminated. The finished instruction card should be attached to a laminated envelope. The puzzle pieces should be stored in the envelope.
3. Some of the activities are reproducible worksheets. The sheets should be stored in laminated folders or envelopes that bear the same worksheet on the outside. The student completes the assignment on the sheet.
4. Some of the activities are to be reproduced, coloured, mounted on a sturdy backing and laminated to make activity cards. The student reads the instructions and completes the activity.

Activity Centre Preparation:

1. Prepare all the activities to be used well in advance of the theme.
2. Make a sign for each centre using a blank card found in the unit.

e.g.

Let's Visit Canada

Hang the sign over the designated activity centre table. If space is a problem, use boxes or plastic bins for your centres. Label each box with the correct sign and place the activities inside. The centre boxes may be stored on shelves, a table or a cart when not in use. Folders may also be made using file folders (letter or legal). Staple the folders along two sides to make holders and place the activities inside. Attach the centre title card to the outside. The activity centre folders may be stored along the chalkboard ledge or in a box.

Student Preparation:

1. Use some sort of notebook or journal for the students to record their completed activities. Binder notebooks that are lined or unlined are quite good. Scrapbooks are useful as well.

2. On the first page of the notebook have the students print the title of the theme and illustrate a picture that corresponds with it.

3. On the second page of the notebook have the students paste in the "Activity Tracking Sheet".

4. Explain briefly the various activity centres and their activities. Indicate the number of activities that each student is expected to complete at each centre and the length of time that will be spent there.

   e.g. Number of Activities: 3; Time: 2 days

5. The students will sign up for the various activity centres on a sign-up board or chart and work at the designated activities. The organization of the students is left up to the teacher in charge. One good method of organization is to divide the students into teams with team captains. Each team may select a name for itself such as names of Canadian animals, birds, etc. (e.g. The High Flying Honkers, The Growling Grizzlies). The students may like to name their teams after career people such as The Magnificent Mounties, The Fantastic Fishers, The Lively Lumberjacks, etc.

7. Teach your students how to organize their record keeping in their Theme Notebooks or Journals. For example, if the student is at Louie Lumberjack's Word Study Centre, he/she should record the name of the centre first on the page. Under the name of the centre the student records the name and number of the activity and the assignment for the activity.

Let's Visit Canada

e.g.

LOUIE LUMBERJACK'S WORD STUDY

Activity Six

A Capital Scramble

Each province and territory found in Canada has a capital city.

Their names are listed below but Louis Lumberjack is a poor speller and the names are spelled incorrectly.

Unscramble the letters and spell each capital city's name correctly.

1. oooTtnr
3. t. J'sShon
4. nwotttChloear
5. genRai
6. ontciredFer
8. yiCt uéecQb
9. seroethiWh
10. vceruonaV
11. gpnWniei
12. monEtnod

Activity Card

Louis Lumberjack's Word Study

Activity Six

A Capital Scramble

1. Toronto
2. Halifax
3. St. John's
4. Charlottetown
5. Regina
6. Fredericton
7. Yellowknife
8. Québec City
9. Whitehorse
10. Vancouver
11. Winnipeg
12. Edmonton

Let's Visit Canada

Student Record Page

As soon as a student completes an activity it must be marked and corrected before going on to the next activity.

Worksheets should be marked and corrected first and then glued in the student record book.

After the completion of each activity the student is to circle the number of each activity completed on the tracking sheet.

7. At the end of the unit have a clean up day. All the students who have completed the required number of activities designated by the teacher should be rewarded for working so hard with a special activity time while the others complete the necessary tasks that were not done.

8. The notebooks should be collected and the theme activities should be evaluated by the classroom teacher. Comments and observations should be noted on an evaluation sheet for each student.

List of Skills

Phonics:

1. Double Vowels
2. Blend Review
3. "Ie" Words
4. Double Consonants
5. Hard/Soft "C"
6. Long/Short/Silent Vowels
7. Digraphs

Brainstorming:

1. Ways Canadians Travel
2. Listing Canadian Facts
3. Reasons to Be Proud
4. Listing Tourist Attractions
5. Listing Canadian Jobs
6. Reasons to Be Proud of One's Province
7. Classifying Animals

Word Study:

1. Alphabetical Order
2. Singular to Plural
3. Syllabication
4. Compound Words
5. Word Search
6. Spelling
7. Crossword Puzzle
8. Word Meanings

Printing/Writing:

1. Copying "O Canada"
2. Copying a Poem
3. Copying a Song
4. Copying Names of Provinces/Territories
5. Copying Names of Canada's Capital Cities
6. Copying Canadian Words

Let's Visit Canada

Map Reading:

1. Locating Canadian Cities
2. Locating Canadian Bays
3. Locating Canadian Lakes
4. Locating Canadian Rivers
5. Locating Canadian Islands
6. Locating Canadian Oceans
7. Matching Geographic Term to Its Meaning
8. Matching Shape Card to Name Card

Creative Writing:

1. Creating a Book on Canada
2. Writing a Canadian Poem
3. Choosing a Story Starter
4. Designing a Canadian Poster
5. Designing a Canadian Postcard

Reading:

1. Answering Riddles
2. Completing Rhymes
3. True or False
4. Recalling Events
5. Noting Details
6. Synonyms/Syllabication
7. Context Clues
8. Listing/Illustrating

Research:

1. Canadian Trivia
2. Nationality Survey
3. Researching a Famous Canadian Place
4. Researching Canadian Animals
5. Researching a Canadian Province

Mathematics:

1. Place Value
2. Expanding Numerals/Sequence
3. Collecting Numerals/Sequence
4. Reading and Writing Numerals/ Sequence
5. Writing Numerals as Words/Comparing Sizes

Let's Visit Canada

Maxine Maple Leaf's Tracking Sheet

Name:______________________________________

In the correct box, print the number of each activity that you complete.

Maxine Maple Leaf's Sounds	Louie Lumberjack's Word Study	Bonhomme's Brainstorming
Fiona Fisher's Map Reading	Cochrane Cowboy's Research	Maggie Miner's Printing/Writing
Farmer Fraser's Creative Writing	Constable Mackenzie's Reading	Iona Inuit's Mathematics

MAXINE MAPLE LEAF'S SOUNDS

Activity One

Double Vowels

Many Canadian Words have double vowels.

e.g. **eats oats boots**

Each double vowel makes **one** sound.

Complete each word in the sentences below with the correct pair of **double vowels** from the box.

ea	oo	ou	ee	ai	ie

1. Gr ___ ___ ndhogs like to live in holes in grassy f ___ ___ lds.
2. Many different kinds of fish live in the Atlantic and Pacific Oc ___ ___ ns .
3. Male d ___ ___ r have large antlers on their h ___ ___ ds.
4. M ___ ___ se love to f ___ ___ d on water lilies.
5. There are thr ___ ___ types of b ___ ___ rs that live in Canada.
6. Farms on the pr ___ ___ ries have large f ___ ___ lds of wh ___ ___ t.
7. The Canada G ___ ___ se flies s ___ ___ th every autumn.
8. A polar b ___ ___ r's favourite f ___ ___ d is the ringed s ___ ___ l.
9. Racc ___ ___ ns love to r ___ ___ d garbage p ___ ___ ls late at night.
10. A b ___ ___ ver uses his bright yellow t ___ ___ th to gnaw on the bark of small tr ___ ___ s.

MAXINE MAPLE LEAF'S SOUNDS

Activity Two

Using Blends

Many Canadian words begin, end or may have a blend inside.

e.g.

green	fa**st**	mu**sk**rat

Use a blend in the box to complete the word to match each meaning.

1. a black and white animal	_____unk
2. large, ugly bear	_____izzly
3. an Arctic bird	_____owy owl
4. red and white Canadian symbol	_____ag
5. Canada has ten of them.	_____ ovinces
6. the way Canadians feel about Canada	_____oud
7. a Canadian language	_____ench
8. flat land in Canada	_____airies
9. grown on the prairies	_____ain
10. a Canadian winter sport	_____ating
11. a round map	_____obe
12. a way to travel in the Yukon	_____owmobile

gr	**fl**	**sk**	**sn**	**pr**	**fl**	**gl**

MAXINE MAPLE LEAF'S SOUNDS

Activity Three

"le Words"

The maple leaf is a symbol of Canada.

The word maple ends with the letters "**le**".

There are other words that end the same way.

Match the "**le**" word found in the maple tree to its correct clue.

1. a large heavy wire

 ____

2. used for eating or working on

 ____

3. a story told by Aesop

 ____

4. part of a barn

 ____

5. a very large spoon

 ____

6. a baby's bed that rocks

 ____

7. a baby's toy

 ____

8. used to move a canoe

 ____

9. a group of cows

 ____

10. stars do it in the sky

 ____

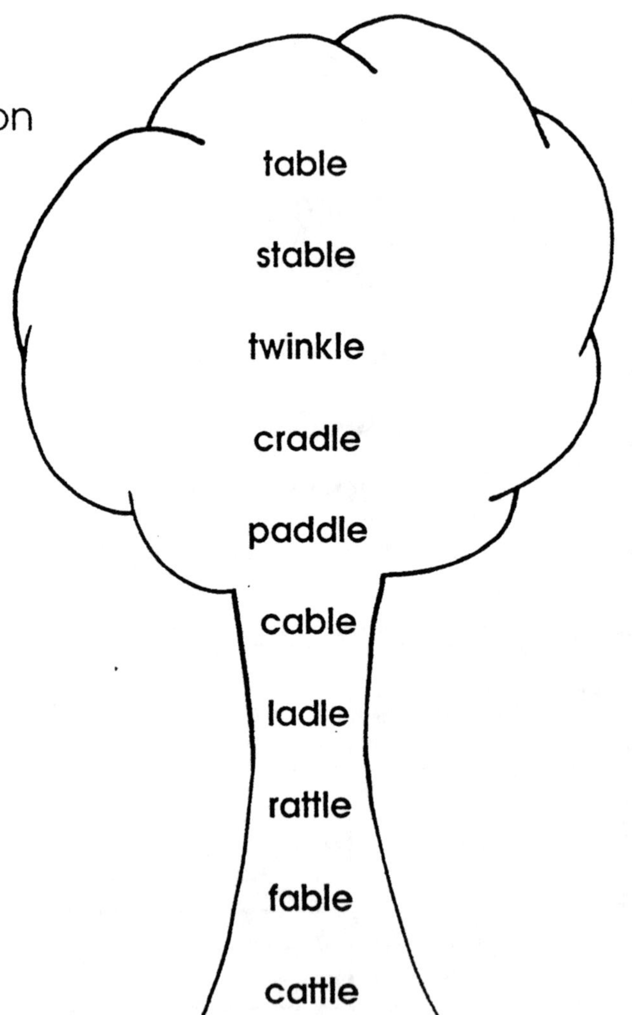

MAXINE MAPLE LEAF'S SOUNDS

Activity Four

Canadian Doubles

Many Canadian words have double letters inside them.

e.g. **Winnipeg**

Copy and **complete** each word below with the correct pair of double letters from the mountains.

rr ff ll mm nn tt ss cc bb

1. ra ___ ___ it
2. co ___ ___ unity
3. Charlo ___ ___ etown
4. O ___ ___ awa
5. cha ___ ___ el
6. vi ___ ___ ages
7. te ___ ___ itory
8. squi ___ ___ el
9. opo ___ ___ um
10. ra ___ ___ oon
11. Ye ___ ___ owknife
12. le ___ ___ ing
13. va ___ ___ ey
14. Ban ___ ___

MAXINE MAPLE LEAF'S SOUNDS

Activity Five

Is it the Hard "C" or the Soft "C"?

In the word "provin<u>c</u>e" we hear the soft "**c**" sound.

In the word "**C**anada" we hear the hard "**c**" sound.

On the chart below classify the words in the flag.

Calgary
city
corn
community
place
canal
mice
capital
caribou
ice
space
rice

Hard C	Soft C
______	______
______	______
______	______
______	______
______	______
______	______

MAXINE MAPLE LEAF'S SOUNDS

Activity Six

Discovering Vowels

Vowels are letters found in most Canadian words.

Vowels can make **two** sounds but sometimes they are **silent**.

<u>Copy</u> the words below neatly.

Circle each vowel sound that you can **hear** and put a **line** through the ones that are **silent**.

Beside each word **name** the ones that you hear.

e.g. | b e a v e r long e |

1. p o l a r b e a r ____________________
2. p o r c u p i n e ____________________
3. c h i p m u n k ____________________
4. p r o v i n c e ____________________
5. m a p l e s y r u p ____________________
6. t o t e m p o l e ____________________
7. M a n i t o b a ____________________
8. N u n a v u t ____________________
9. v i l l a g e ____________________
10. W h i t e h o r s e ____________________

MAXINE MAPLE LEAF'S SOUNDS

Activity Seven

Working With Digraphs

"**Ch, sh, th** and **wh**" are sounds called digraphs.

Copy and **complete** each sentence below with the correct **digraph**.

1. More _____ an one _____ ird of Canada's people live in Ontario.

2. _____ ere are many kinds of _____ ales living in oceans near Canada.

3. Many striped _____ ipmunks live in the forests found in Canada.

4. The wood _____ uck dug his burrow in the side of a grassy hill.

5. People in Newfoundland fi _____ to make a living.

6. Farmers _____ o live on the prairies grow _____ eat in _____ eir large fields.

7. The capital city of the Yukon is called _____ itehorse.

8. Cowboys work on ran _____ es found in Alberta.

9. People travel to _____ ur _____ ill, Manitoba to wat _____ the polar bears.

10. People in Québec speak mainly Fren _____.

LOUIE LUMBERJACK'S WORD STUDY

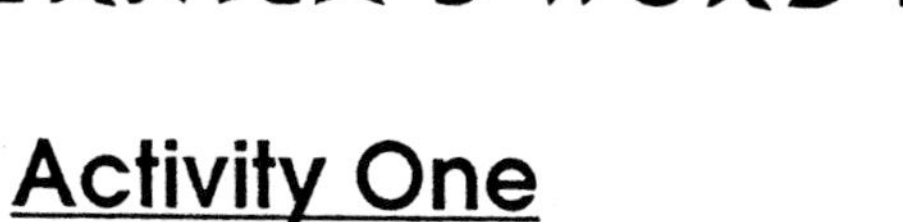

Activity One

Canadian Word Order

Montréal is a very large city in Québec.

There are many other cities and towns throughout Canada.

Copy the names of other places found in Canada in the correct **alphabetical** order.

Yarmouth	**Dauphin**
Battleford	**Jasper**
Edmonton	**Inuvik**
Neepawa	**Thunder Bay**
Amherst	**Vancouver**
Hamilton	**Whitehorse**
Kingston	**Ottawa**
Fredericton	**London**
Saskatoon	**Moncton**
Regina	**Goderich**
Pond Inlet	**Calgary**
Québec City	**Yellowknife**

LOUIE LUMBERJACK'S WORD STUDY

Activity Two

Make it mean more than one!

A village is a small place where people live.

There are many villages in Canada.

The word **village** is a **singular** word.

The word **villages** is a **plural** word.

Copy the words below neatly.

Beside each one write its **plural form.**

1. maple leaf ______________________
2. territory ______________________
3. province ______________________
4. city ______________________
5. moose ______________________
6. community ______________________
7. deer ______________________
8. Canada Goose ______________________
9. Arctic Fox ______________________
10. country ______________________
11. ocean ______________________
12. walrus ______________________

LOUIE LUMBERJACK'S WORD STUDY

Activity Three

Canadian Syllables

Toronto is the capital city of **Ontario.**

Ontario has **four** syllables.

Copy the names of the provinces and territories below.

Beside each name write the **number of syllables** that you can hear.

e.g.

1. Québec _____
2. Nova Scotia _____
3. Newfoundland _____
4. Manitoba _____
5. Alberta _____
6. Prince Edward Island _____
7. British Columbia _____
8. Saskatchewan _____
9. New Brunswick _____
10. Ontario _____
11. Yukon _____
12. Nunavut _____
13. Northwest Territories _____

LOUIE LUMBERJACK'S WORD STUDY

Activity Four

Canadian Compounds

Charlottetown is the capital city of Prince Edward Island.

Charlottetown is a **compound** word.

Use the compound words in the box to **match** the clues.

Write each word on the correct line.

Charlottetown	**lumberjack**	**cowboys**
groundhog	**neighbourhood**	**Yellowknife**
Whitehorse	**evergreen**	**Newfoundland**
waterfalls		

1. sometimes it sees its shadow in February ______________
2. capital of Prince Edward Island______________
3. a place you live in ______________
4. capital of the Yukon ______________
5. capital of the Northwest Territories ______________
6. water moving over a high place ______________
7. a person who cuts down trees ______________
8. an island province______________
9. a tree with needles ______________
10. men who work on ranches ______________

LOUIE LUMBERJACK'S WORD STUDY

Activity Five

Province and Territory Search

Explore the word search and find the names of Canada's provinces and territories. Circle each one.

A	N	O	R	T	H	W	E	S	T	T	E	R	R	I	T	O	R	I	E	S
P	O	B	Q	A	M	V	D	C	L	K	Z	Q	D	J	Y	E	A	P	F	A
H	V	P	C	B	R	N	U	Q	N	U	N	A	V	U	T	O	U	Y	B	S
J	A	T	A	R	D	B	E	I	W	R	D	U	X	X	N	I	G	O	H	K
A	S	A	K	I	S	E	B	O	O	C	S	R	N	C	B	T	G	C	A	A
U	C	I	B	T	D	T	F	N	B	C	A	B	S	F	E	U	Z	Z	H	T
K	O	A	L	I	J	V	L	T	G	K	H	H	T	M	C	W	B	Q	G	C
Q	T	G	C	S	I	B	L	A	U	U	V	D	T	A	T	F	M	F	H	H
V	I	R	M	H	W	J	A	R	J	H	M	C	I	N	S	I	C	J	R	E
R	A	S	Y	C	F	N	H	I	K	E	J	E	C	I	W	G	U	D	N	W
T	X	Z	P	O	I	C	Z	O	K	G	V	E	M	T	K	F	L	V	Y	A
A	Q	I	S	L	A	Q	G	R	Q	S	L	Q	D	O	N	O	D	M	O	N
C	U	B	B	U	X	K	C	I	W	S	N	U	R	B	W	E	N	W	P	G
H	E	T	Y	M	J	O	W	J	U	S	M	R	E	A	W	O	A	V	X	P
V	B	D	I	B	Y	L	P	Y	K	D	V	X	K	U	R	P	L	F	N	L
A	E	B	Z	I	T	Z	X	J	W	K	U	E	J	Y	F	M	D	X	Q	Z
F	C	H	E	A	C	W	M	A	L	A	L	O	V	M	W	R	N	S	J	Y
A	K	B	G	X	V	S	D	H	X	L	T	N	I	S	M	N	U	N	L	P
E	J	Y	U	K	O	N	Y	D	G	B	R	H	P	Q	G	I	O	M	O	I
C	G	L	F	G	B	S	E	N	Y	E	F	R	O	K	Q	O	F	H	T	Z
V	I	Z	W	C	A	C	Z	T	M	R	L	P	E	Q	O	F	W	N	P	K
H	Y	D	A	M	X	U	D	B	Z	T	E	N	S	P	R	J	E	T	U	I
F	P	R	I	N	C	E	E	D	W	A	R	D	I	S	L	A	N	D	O	Q

LOUIE LUMBERJACK'S WORD STUDY

Activity Six

A Capital Scramble

Each province and territory found in Canada has a capital city.

Their names are listed below but Louis Lumberjack is a poor speller and the names are spelled incorrectly.

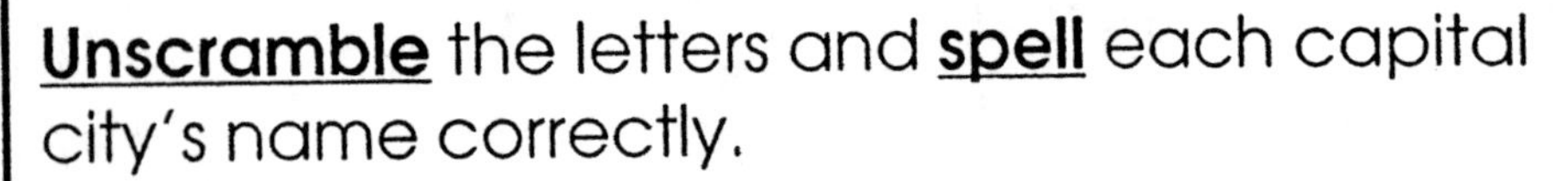

Unscramble the letters and **spell** each capital city's name correctly.

1. o o o T t n r ______________________
2. a f i l a x H ______________________
3. t. J 's S h o n ______________________
4. n w o t t t C h l o e a r ______________________
5. g e n R a i ______________________
6. o n t c i r e d F e r ______________________
7. k n i f e Y w o e i f ______________________
8. y i C t u e é c Q b ______________________
9. s e r o e t h i W h ______________________
10. v c e r u o n a V ______________________
11. g p n W n i e i ______________________
12. m o n E t n o d ______________________

LOUIE LUMBERJACK'S WORD STUDY
Activity Seven
Canada's Crossword Puzzle
Think Canada!
Complete the crossword puzzle carefully.
Read the clues.

LOUIE LUMBERJACK'S WORD STUDY

Activity Seven

Canada's Crossword Puzzle Clues

Across:

1. Canada's national emblem
2. The Yukon is one of them.
3. Canada's national bird
4. It is a new territory.
5. Grain that is grown on the Prairies.
6. One of the colours found on Canada's flag.

Down:

1. The Rockies are high ones.
2. The short way to write "mountie".
3. Canada is the second largest one.
4. It is a red and white Canadian symbol.
5. The capital city of Canada
6. Canada has ten of them.
7. Canada's national animal
8. The name of Canada's national anthem

LOUIE LUMBERJACK'S WORD STUDY

Activity Eight

What is it?

There are many different land forms in Canada.

Copy and **complete** each sentence with the correct word from the box.

country
village
river
ocean
city
provinces
lake
mountains
island

1. An ______________ is a large body of salt water.
2. A ______________ is a large body of fresh water.
3. A __________________________ is a long body of flowing water.
4. Canada is made of parts called ______________.
5. A ______________ is a large community where people live and work.
6. __________________________ are very high hills.
7. A ______________ is a very small community.
8. A ______________ is a land where many people live.
9. An ______________________ is a piece of land completely surrounded by water.

BONHOMME'S BRAINSTORMING

Activity One

Travelling in Canada

People travel in Canada in many different ways.

Canadians who live near the oceans travel by boat from place to place.

Canadians who live in the territories travel by snowmobile and plane.

Think of other ways people travel in Canada.

Make a chart like the one below.

e.g.

Canadian Travel

car

On the chart **illustrate** the different ways Canadians travel.

Label each way.

BONHOMME'S BRAINSTORMING

Activity Two

Just the Canadian Facts Please!

How well do you know Canada?

Try to think of as many facts as you can.

Draw a large flag like the one below.

On the flag **print** the facts.

e.g.

Canada is ....

Canada has.............................

Canada is..............................

BONHOMME'S BRAINSTORMING

Activity Three

Canadians Are Proud People

Canada is a great country where people are free and live well.

Canadians are very **proud** of their country.

Think of **reasons** why they should be proud.

Draw a large maple leaf.

On the maple leaf **print** the reasons.

e.g.

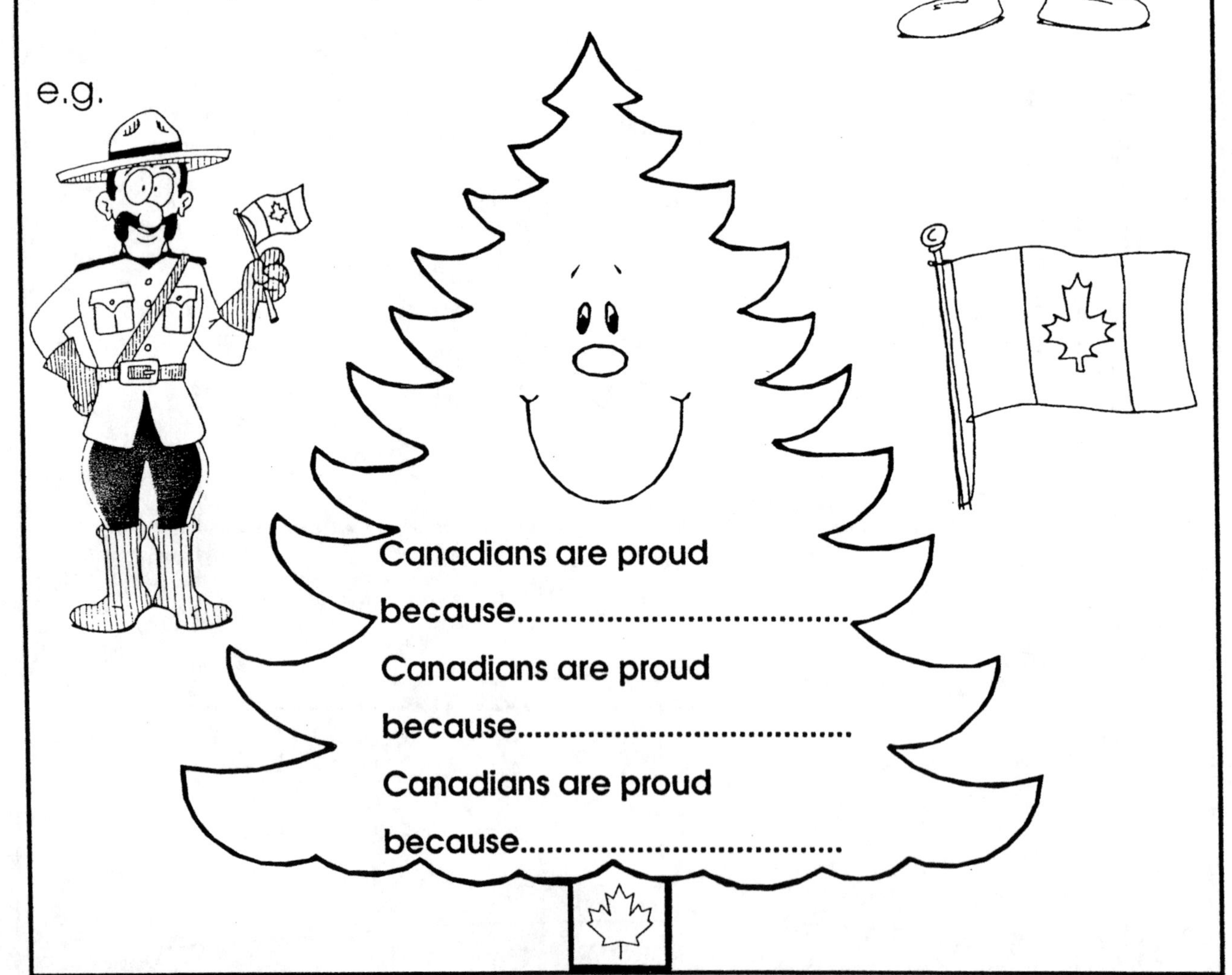

BONHOMME'S BRAINSTORMING

Activity Four

Interesting Places to Visit

Canadians live in different parts of Canada.

Each part has interesting places to visit.

Pretend that you are having a visitor coming from another country.

Make a **list** of the interesting places where you could take your visitor.

e.g.

Interesting Places

1. Ottawa
2. CN Tower
3. Edmonton Mall
4. ______________________
5. ______________________
6. ______________________
7. ______________________
8. ______________________
9. ______________________
10. ______________________

BONHOMME'S BRAINSTORMING

Activity Five

Working Canadians

In Canada, people work at many different types of jobs.

Think of the different places in your community where people work.

Make a **list** of the different jobs or the places people work in Canada.

Illustrate your mother or father at work in your community.

e.g.

Kinds of Jobs	My Mom/Dad at Work
1. teacher 2. doctor 3. nurse 4. ________ 5. ________ 6. ________ 7. ________ 8. ________ 9. ________	

BONHOMME'S BRAINSTORMING

Activity Six

I'm proud to live in.........

In which province or territory do you live?

How do you feel about it?

Do you feel proud?

List reasons why you are proud of your province.

Try to think of **three** good ones.

Begin each reason like the example below.

e.g.

I am proud of Ontario because the people are friendly and kind.

I am proud of Ontario because it has many interesting places to visit.

I am proud of Ontario because it has beautiful lakes and forests.

BONHOMME'S BRAINSTORMING

Activity Seven

Classifying Fun!

Animals make their homes in many places all over Canada.

Some live in trees, in water, on land, in the air or in the mountains.

Make a **chart** like the one below.

On the chart **classify** the following animals.

e.g.

Forest Animals
Tree Animals
Water Animals
Air Animals
Mountain Animals

mountain lion | **lynx**
squirrel | **deer**
beaver | **chipmunk**
eagle | **fox**
mountain goat | **black bear**
grizzly bear | **trout**
moose | **rabbit**
wolf | **muskrat**
seagull | **salmon**
skunk | **walrus**
porcupine | **raccoon**
Canada Goose | **flounder**
opossum | **cod**

FIONA FISHER'S MAP READING

Activity One

Canadian Cities

Canada has many large cities.

A city is a large place where many people live.

Look at a map of Canada.

Find the names of **ten** cities.

Write their names in a list.

e.g.

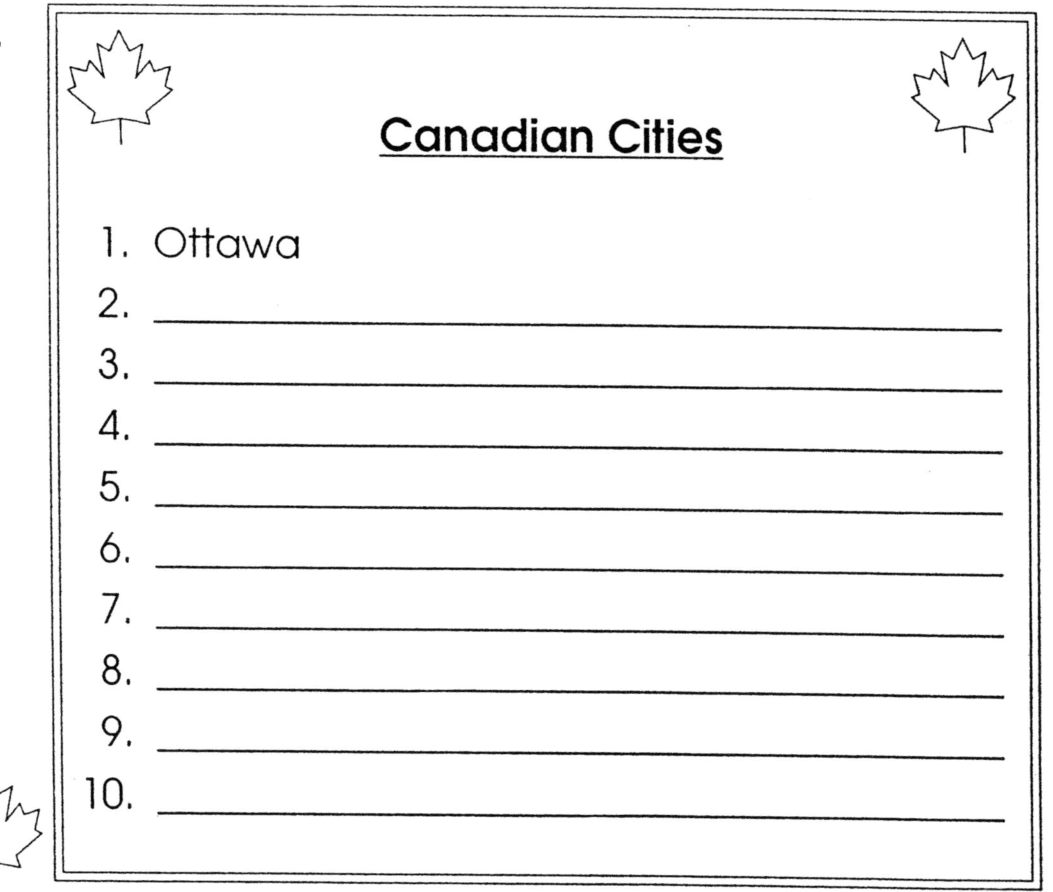

Canadian Cities

1. Ottawa
2. ____________________
3. ____________________
4. ____________________
5. ____________________
6. ____________________
7. ____________________
8. ____________________
9. ____________________
10. ____________________

FIONA FISHER'S MAP READING

Activity Two

Canadian Bays

A bay is a part of an ocean, sea or lake extending into the land.

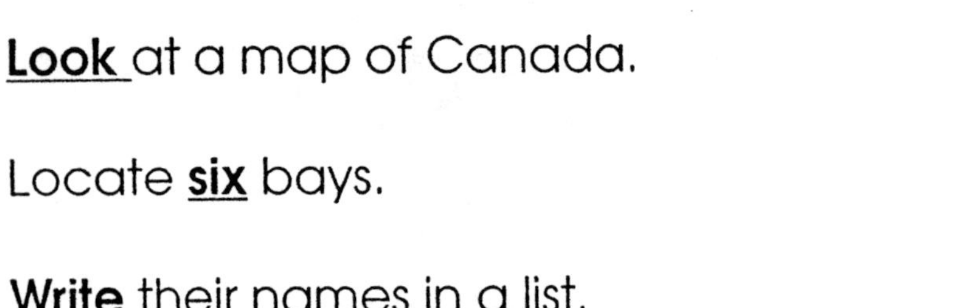

Look at a map of Canada.

Locate **six** bays.

Write their names in a list.

e.g.

Canadian Bays

1. Hudson Bay
2. ______________________________
3. ______________________________
4. ______________________________
5. ______________________________
6. ______________________________

FIONA FISHER'S MAP READING

Activity Three

Canadian Lakes

A lake is a body of fresh or salt water surrounded by land.

Look at a map of Canada.

Locate the names of **ten** lakes found in Canada.

Write their names in a list.

e.g.

Canadian Lakes

1. Lake Ontario
2. ______
3. ______
4. ______
5. ______
6. ______
7. ______
8. ______
9. ______
10. ______

FIONA FISHER'S MAP READING

Activity Four

Canadian Rivers

There are many small and large rivers flowing in Canada.

A river is a body of flowing water.

Explore a map of Canada.

Locate the names of **ten** rivers.

Write their names in a list.

e.g.

Canadian Rivers

1. St. Lawrence
2. ______________________
3. ______________________
4. ______________________
5. ______________________
6. ______________________
7. ______________________
8. ______________________
9. ______________________
10. ______________________

FIONA FISHER'S MAP READING

Activity Five

Canadian Islands

Newfoundland is one of Canada's largest islands.

An island is a piece of land completely surrounded by water.

Explore a map of Canada.

Locate the names of **ten** islands found in Canada.

Write their names in a list.

e.g.

Canadian Islands

1. Newfoundland
2. ______________________
3. ______________________
4. ______________________
5. ______________________
6. ______________________
7. ______________________
8. ______________________
9. ______________________
10. ______________________

FIONA FISHER'S MAP READING

Activity Six

Oceans of the World

The Atlantic ocean is found on Canada's east coast.

An ocean is a large body of salt water.

Look at a map of the world or a globe.

Locate the names of **five** oceans.

Write their names in a list.

e.g.

Oceans of the World

1. Atlantic Ocean
2. ______________________
3. ______________________
4. ______________________
5. ______________________

FIONA FISHER'S MAP READING

Activity Seven

Canadian Land Forms

There are many different types of land forms found in Canada.

In the envelope are some word cards and meaning cards.

Match the word cards to their meaning cards.

e.g.

peak	the highest point of a mountain

FIONA FISHER'S MAP READING

Activity Eight

Matching Parts of Canada

Canada has ten provinces and three territories.

Each one has a capital city.

The provinces and territories have different shapes and sizes.

In the envelope are some province and territory shape cards, name cards and capital city name cards.

Match the province and territorial shape to its name and capital city.

e.g.

Halifax	Nova Scotia

Fiona Fisher's Map Reading - Activity #7; Word/Meaning Matching: Cut out the word cards and meaning cards. Mount the cards on a sturdy backing and laminate. Store the cards in an envelope. Attach the instruction card to the envelope. The student will match the land form to its meaning.

channel	a narrow body of water between two pieces of land that joins two large bodies of water
canal	a narrow, man-made waterway used for ships
bay	a part of an ocean, sea or lake extending into the land
hill	a slightly higher point of land rising above the land surrounding it
island	a piece of land completely surrounded by water
lake	a body of fresh or salted water entirely surrounded by land

Fiona Fisher's Map Reading - Activity #7: Word/Meaning Matching: Cut out the word cards and meaning cards. Mount the cards on a sturdy backing and laminate. Store the cards in an envelope. Attach the instruction card to the envelope. The student will match the land form to its meaning.

mountain	a very high, steep hill
ocean	a large body of salt water
peninsula	a piece of land extending into the ocean or sea almost surrounded by water.
plateau	high, flat land
sea	a large body of salt water smaller than an ocean
valley	a long, narrow piece of land between two high areas

<u>**Fiona Fisher's Map Reading - Activity #8; Province/Territory/Capital City Matching:**</u> Cut out the province shape cards, province name cards and capital city name cards. Mount the cards on a sturdy backing and laminate. Store the cards in an envelope. Attach the instruction card to an envelope. The student will match the province shape card to its name and capital city.

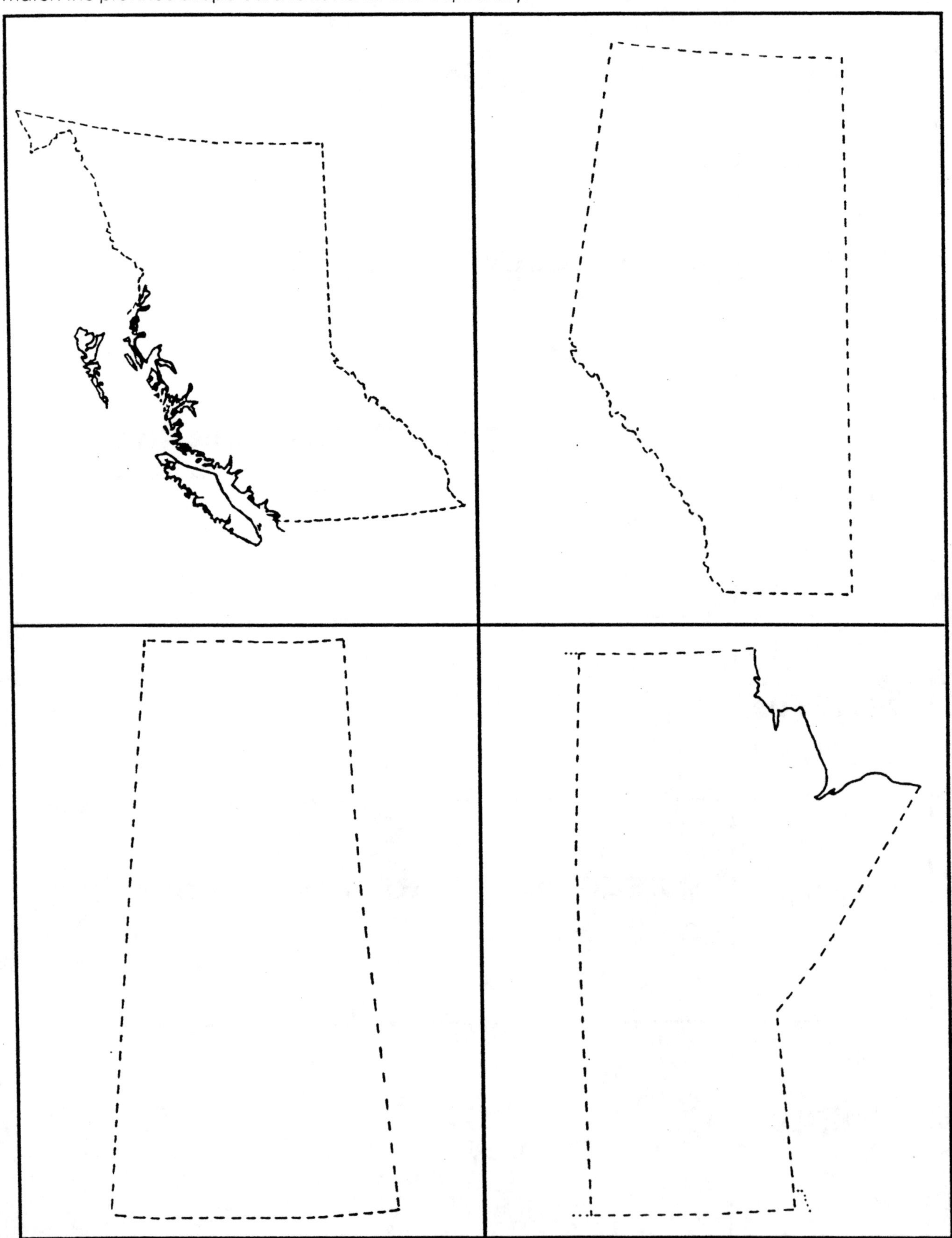

Fiona Fisher's Map Reading - Activity #8; Province/Territory/Capital City Matching: Cut out the province shape cards, province name cards and capital city name cards. Mount the cards on a sturdy backing and laminate. Store the cards in an envelope. Attach the instruction card to an envelope. The student will match the province shape card to its name and capital city.

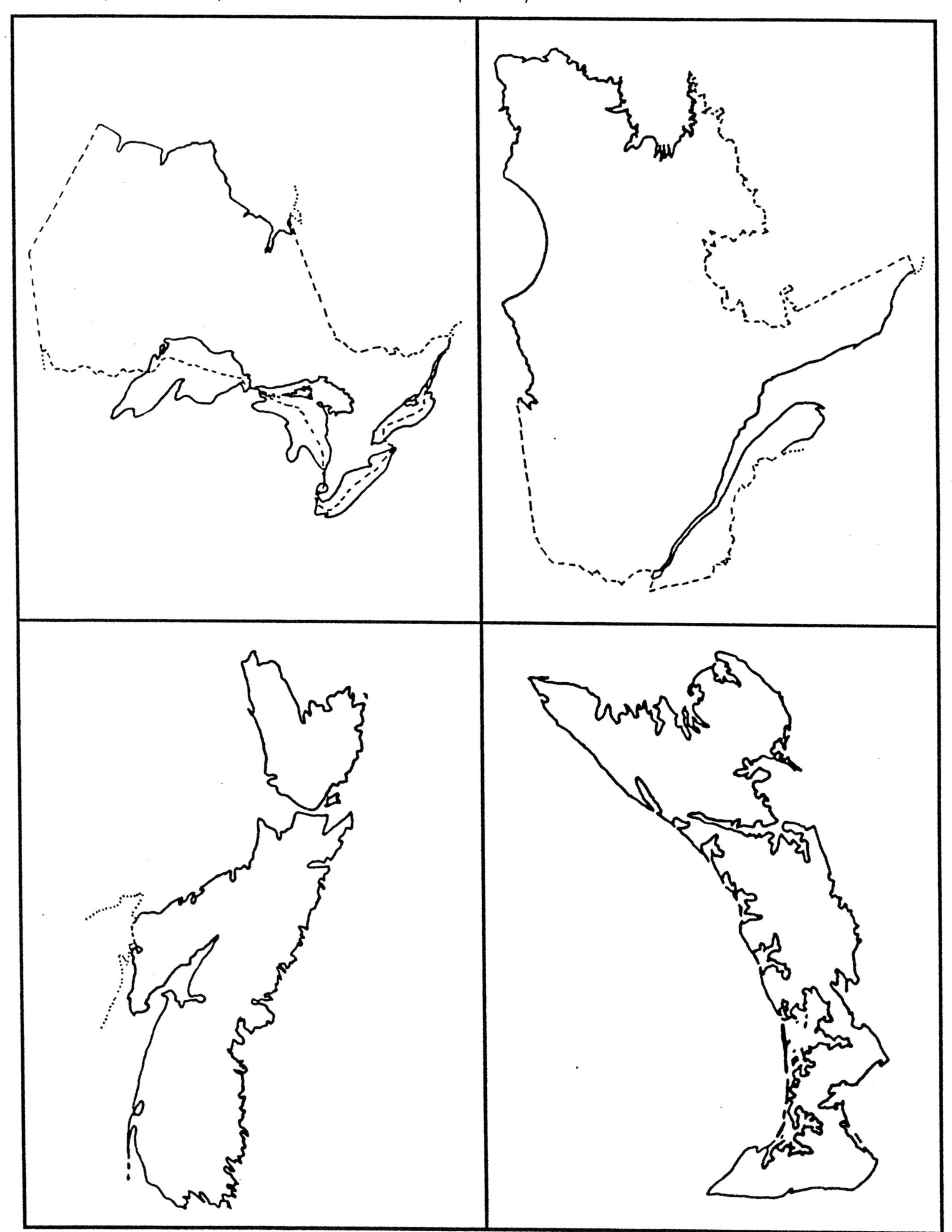

Fiona Fisher's Map Reading - Activity #8; Province/Territory/Capital City Matching: Cut out the province shape cards, province name cards and capital city name cards. Mount the cards on a sturdy backing and laminate. Store the cards in an envelope. Attach the instruction card to an envelope. The student will match the province shape card to its name and capital city.

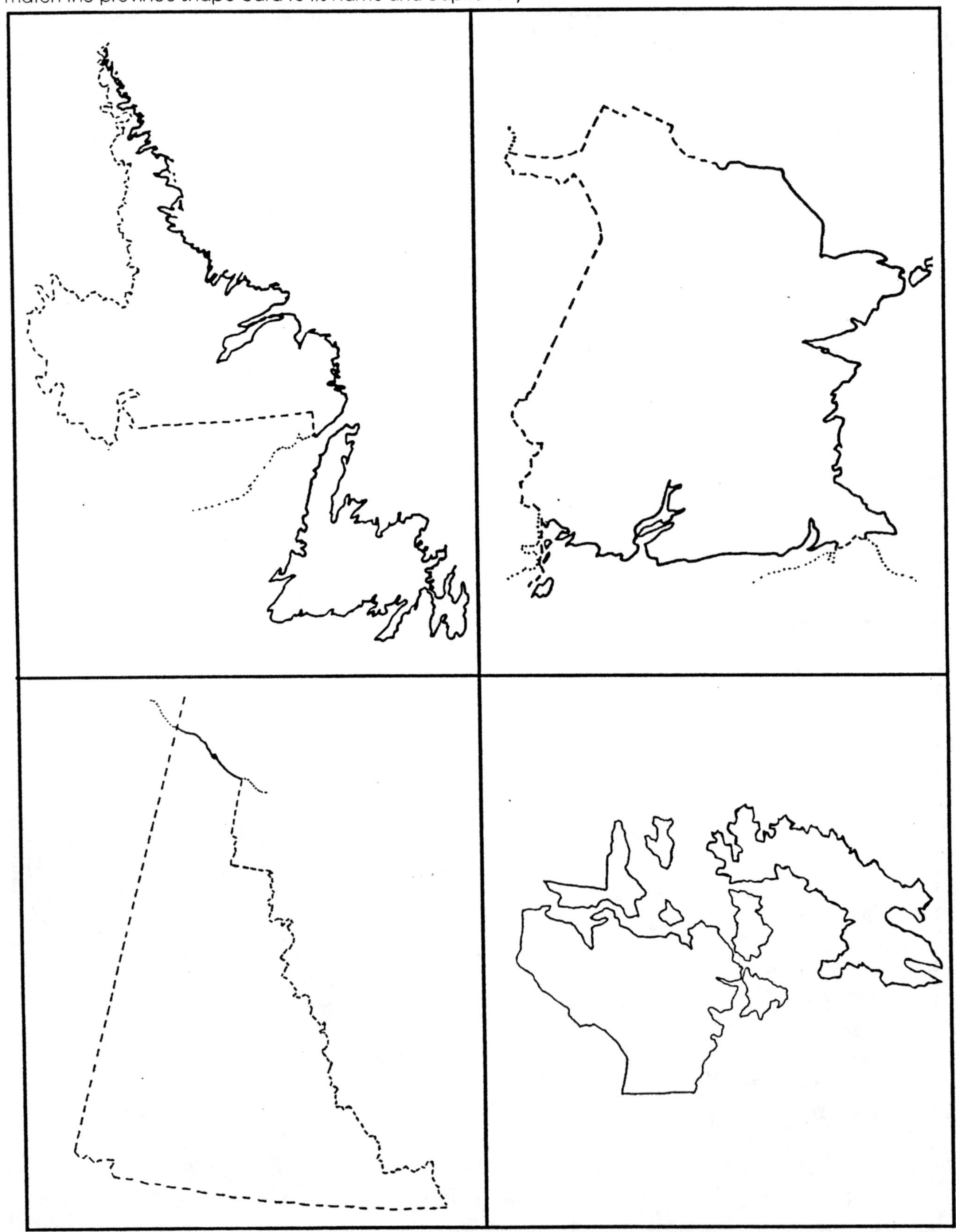

Fiona Fisher's Map Reading - Activity #8; Province/Territory/Capital City Matching: Cut out the province shape cards, province name cards and capital city name cards. Mount the cards on a sturdy backing and laminate. Store the cards in an envelope. Attach the instruction card to an envelope. The student will match the province shape card to its name and capital city.

Fiona Fisher's Map Reading - Activity #8; Province/Territory/Capital City Matching: Cut out the province shape cards, province name cards and capital city name cards. Mount the cards on a sturdy backing and laminate. Store the cards in an envelope. Attach the instruction card to an envelope. The student will match the province shape card to its name and capital city.

Québec	Yukon
Nunavut	Northwest Territories
St. John's	Charlottetown
Regina	Winnipeg
Toronto	Fredericton
Victoria	Edmonton

Fiona Fisher's Map Reading - Activity #8: Province/Territory/Capital City Matching: Cut out the province shape cards, province name cards and capital city name cards. Mount the cards on a sturdy backing and laminate. Store the cards in an envelope. Attach the instruction card to an envelope. The student will match the province shape card to its name and capital city.

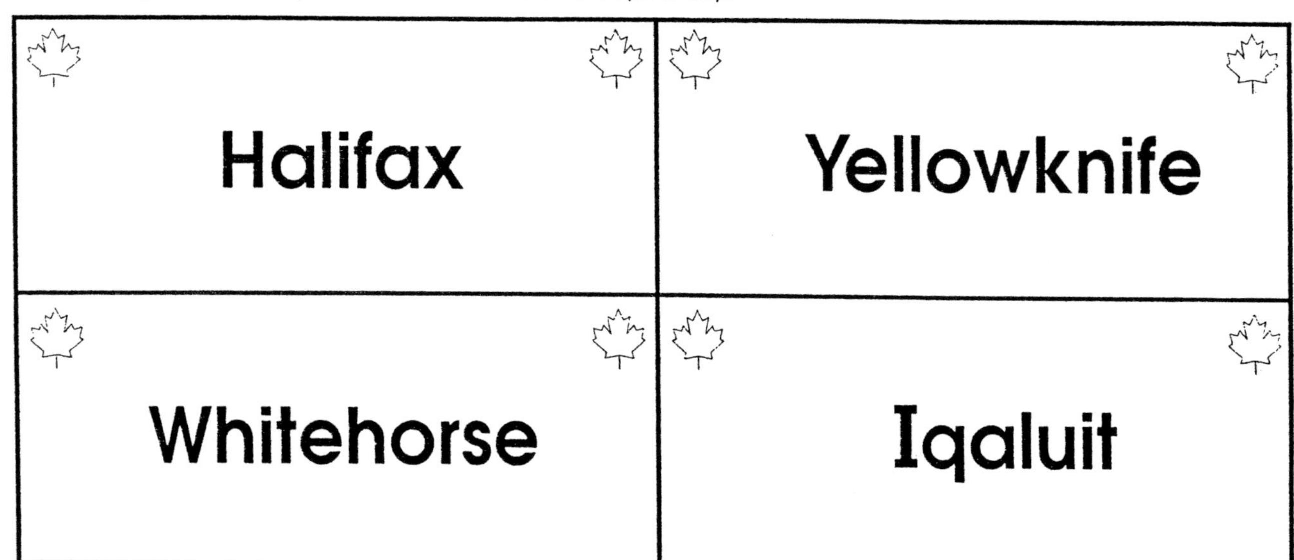

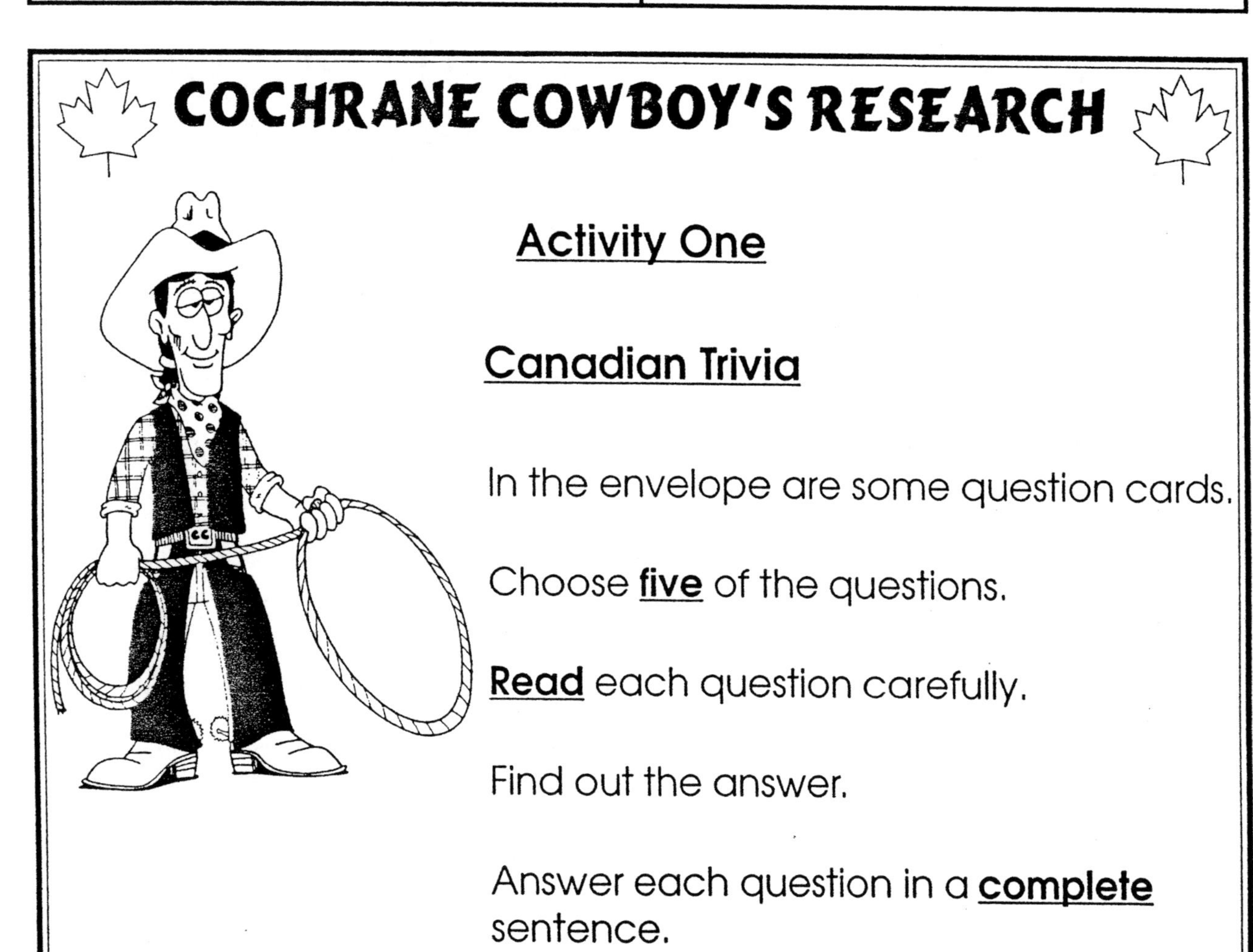

Cochrane Cowboy's Research - Activity One: Locating Answers: Cut out the question cards, mount on a sturdy backing and laminate. Store the cards in an envelope. Attach the instruction card. The student will choose five questions, research to find out the answers and record the answers in complete sentences.

1. Who is Canada's Prime Minister today?	**5.** What are the two main languages spoken in Canada?
2. Which province has the largest population?	**6.** Which province in Canada is the largest in size?
3. Which province in Canada is the smallest in size?	**7.** What are the names of the Atlantic provinces?
4. Which province is found in the middle of Canada?	**8.** Which provinces are islands?

Cochrane Cowboy's Research - Activity One; Locating Answers: Cut out the question cards, mount on a sturdy backing and laminate. Store the cards in an envelope. Attach the instruction card. The student will choose five questions, research to find out the answers and record the answers in complete sentences.

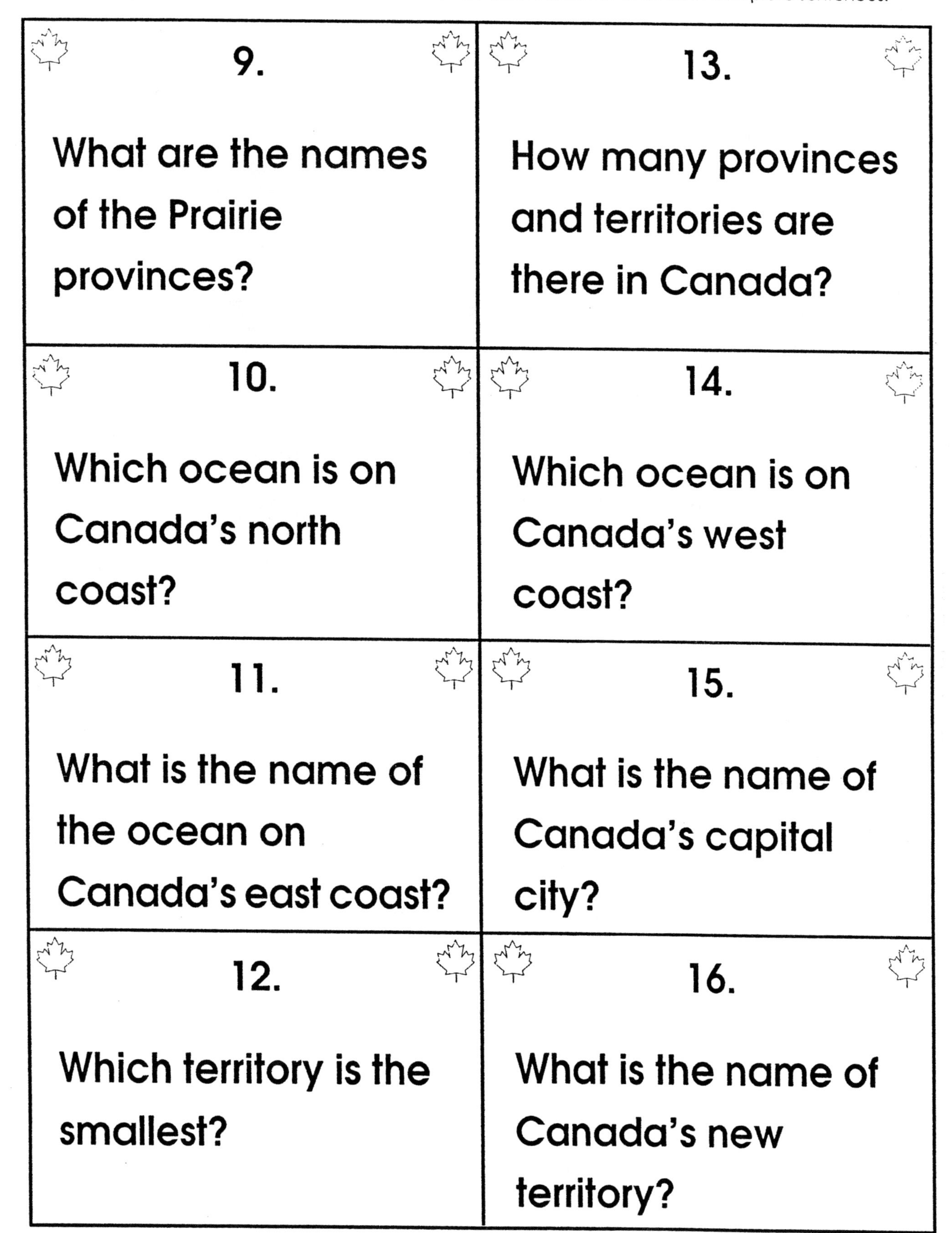

9.

What are the names of the Prairie provinces?

13.

How many provinces and territories are there in Canada?

10.

Which ocean is on Canada's north coast?

14.

Which ocean is on Canada's west coast?

11.

What is the name of the ocean on Canada's east coast?

15.

What is the name of Canada's capital city?

12.

Which territory is the smallest?

16.

What is the name of Canada's new territory?

COCHRANE COWBOY'S RESEARCH

Activity Two

Where were you born?

Some Canadians were born in Canada and some were born in other countries.

Survey your class to find out where your classmates were born and where their parents and grandparents were born.

Survey	Checks	Total
1. I was born in Canada.		
2. I was born in another country.		
3. My parents were born in Canada.		
4. My parents were born in another country.		
5. My grandparents were born in Canada.		
6. My grandparents were not born in Canada.		

Results of My Survey

Classmates born in Canada __________

Classmates not born in Canada __________

Parents born in Canada __________

Parents not born in Canada __________

Grandparents born in Canada __________

Grandparents not born in Canada __________

COCHRANE COWBOY'S RESEARCH

Activity Three

A Famous Canadian Place

Canada is filled with many interesting places to visit.

e.g.

Casa Loma, Toronto

Choose **one** of the famous places below.

Capilano Suspension Bridge	**CN Tower**
Parliament Buildings	**Banff**
Calgary Stampede	**Casa Loma**
Rocky Mountains	**Percé Rock**
Kings Landing	**Bata Shoe Museum**
Fortress of Louisbourg	**Green Gables**
L'Anse aux Meadows	**Sky Dome**
Jack London's Cabin	**Cape Spear**

Research the one that you chose.

Complete the worksheet on the place that you chose.

COCHRANE COWBOY'S REPORT

A FAMOUS CANADIAN PLACE

Name of Place: ______________________________

Location: ______________________________

____

____

Interesting Facts: (Try to find five.)

____

____

____

____

____

____

____

____

____

____

____

Illustrate the famous place.

COCHRANE COWBOY'S RESEARCH

Activity Four

Who Lives in a Canadian Forest?

In Canada's forests many wild animals make their homes.

e.g.

Choose **one** of the Canadian animals below that interests you.

beaver	**porcupine**	**beaver**	**wolf**
moose	**chipmunk**	**skunk**	**fox**
raccoon	**polar bear**	**caribou**	**otter**
squirrel	**opossum**	**bobcat**	**muskrat**
lynx	**mountain lion**	**deer**	**elk**
rabbit	**mountain sheep**	**coyote**	**mole**

Research the animal that you chose.

Complete the work sheet on the animal that you chose.

COCHRANE COWBOY'S REPORT

A CANADIAN ANIMAL

Name: ______________________________

Appearance: (Describe how it looks)

____
____
____
____
____

Home: (Describe its home)

____
____
____
____
____

Food: (List the things that it eats)

____
____
____

Enemies: (Tell who it fears)

____
____
____

Habits: (Tell about things it always does)

____
____
____
____

On another sheet of paper illustrate the animal.

COCHRANE COWBOY'S RESEARCH

Activity Five

Writing About A Province or Territory

In Canada there are ten provinces and three territories.

Provinces:

Prince Edward Island	*Ontario*
Nova Scotia	*Manitoba*
New Brunswick	*Saskatoon*
Newfoundland	*Alberta*
Québec	*British Columbia*

Territories:

Northwest Territories *The Yukon*	*Nunavut*

Choose a province or a territory that you find interesting.

Research it

Complete the worksheet on the one that you chose.

Write the information in complete sentences.

COCHRANE COWBOY'S REPORT

A Canadian Province or Territory

Province/Territory: ____________________

____

Capital City: ____________________

Size and Location: ____________________

____

____

____

Population: ____________________

Products: ____________________

____

____

____

Interesting Facts: (Try to find six)

____

____

____

____

____

____

____

____

Illustrate the provincial flower and the provincial flag on another sheet of paper.

MAGGIE MINER'S PRINTING/WRITING

Activity One

"O Canada"

"O Canada" is the name of Canada's national anthem.

Look in a songbook for the words to "O Canada".

Copy **one** of the verses in your best printing or writing.

MAGGIE MINER'S PRINTING/WRITING

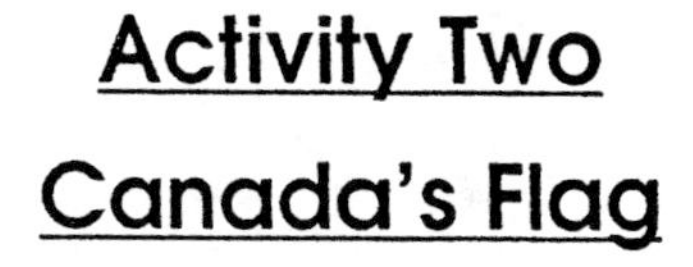

Activity Two

Canada's Flag

Copy the poem in your best printing or writing.

Shout loudly for Canada's flag!
Salute proudly Canada's flag!
The flag of our country.
Its colours brighten up the sky,
As it flutters way up high
A beautiful sight to see!
Protecting you and me.

Ruth Solski

MAGGIE MINER'S PRINTING/WRITING

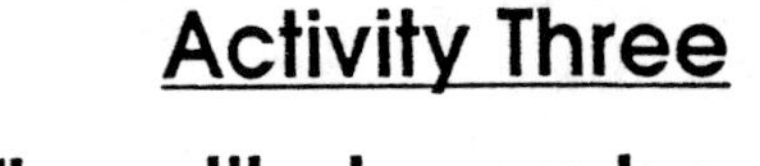

Activity Three

There'll always be........

Copy the poem in your best printing or writing.

There'll always be a Canada
To stretch from coast to coast.
A land of freedom and safety,
About which we can proudly boast.

There'll always be a Canada
A land for future years.
A place for liberty and love
Where people live free of fears.

Ruth Solski

MAGGIE MINER'S PRINTING/WRITING

Activity Four

Parts of Canada

Copy the names of Canada's provinces and territories in your best printing or writing.

Prince Edward Island	**Ontario**
Saskatchewan	**Manitoba**
British Columbia	**Alberta**
Newfoundland	**Yukon**
New Brunswick	**Quebec**
Northwest Territories	**Nunavut**
Nova Scotia	

MAGGIE MINER'S PRINTING/WRITING

Activity Five

Copy the names of Canada's capital cities in your best printing or writing.

St. John's
Fredericton
Whitehorse
Yellowknife
Charlottetown
Québec City
Edmonton
Regina
Calgary
Iqaluit
Winnipeg
Toronto
Halifax

MAGGIE MINER'S PRINTING/WRITING

Activity Six

Canadian Words

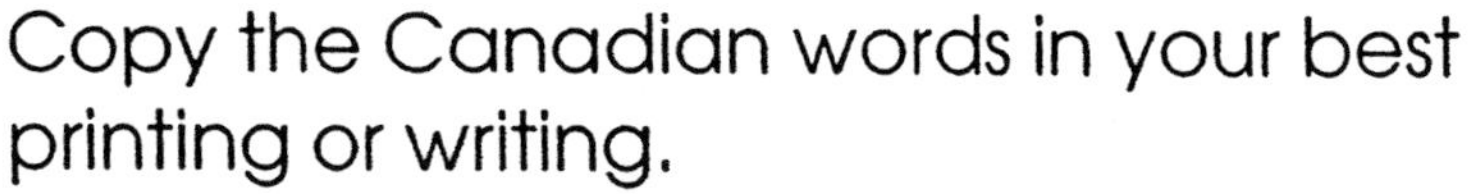

Copy the Canadian words in your best printing or writing.

Canada
Canadians
maple leaf
beaver
country
emblem
provinces
territories
Prime Minister
Premier
French
English

FARMER FRASER'S CREATIVE WRITING

Activity One

Create a Canadian Book!

There have been many books written about Canada.

e.g.

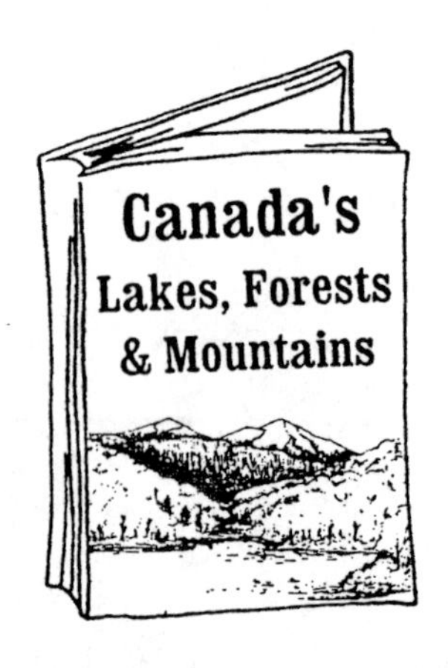

Make your own book about Canada.

It may be about:

Canadian Animals
Canadian Places
A Canadian Province
Canadian Wild Flowers
Canadian Flags
Canadian People
Canadian Birds
Canadian Fish
Canadian Workers
A Canadian Province
A Canadian Capital City

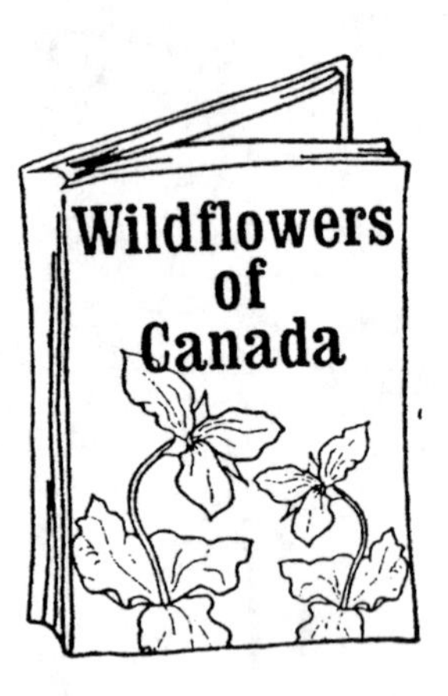

In your book draw pictures and print information about your topic.

FARMER FRASER'S CREATIVE WRITING

Activity Two

Write a Canadian Poem

Each province in Canada has special features and places.

Print the name of your province vertically

e.g.

Ontario
Nickel
Terrific
Apples
Rivers
Industrial
Ottawa

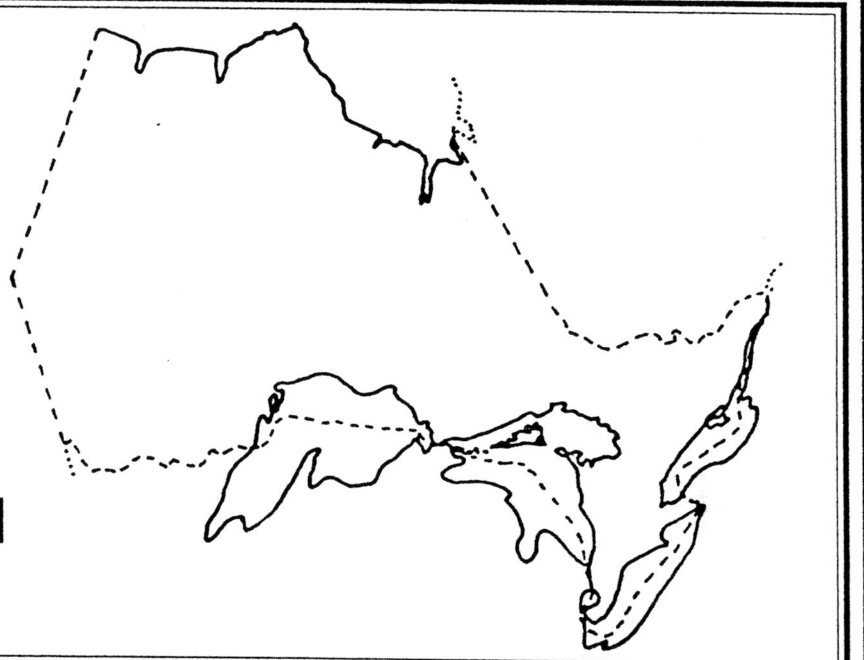

Think of words that describe your province or the things that it contains.

Each word must **begin** with a letter in your province's name.

Illustrate your one word poem.

FARMER FRASER'S CREATIVE WRITING

Activity Three

Write a Story

Choose **one** of the story starters below.

Copy the story starter neatly.

Complete it.

Add more sentences to it and write a story.

Story Starters

1. If I wanted to live in another province I would choose

   _______________ because ....

2. If I wanted to visit a famous place in Canada I would choose

   _______________ because ....

3. If I could change something in Canada I would ___________

   because ....

4. If I could be Prime Minister of Canada for a day I would

   _______________ because ....

5. If I could be a famous Canadian I would want to be

   _______________ because ....

FARMER FRASER'S CREATIVE WRITING

Activity Four

A Canadian Poster

Posters of Canada are often displayed in stores and tourist agencies.

e.g.

Design a poster advertising a place that is special in Canada.

Print a caption about it on your poster.

Colour your poster neatly and use lots of bright colours.

FARMER FRASER'S CREATIVE WRITING

Activity Five

A Canadian Postcard

A postcard has a picture of a place on one side and a space to write a note and an address on the back.

When we visit another country or another province we often send postcards to our friends and relatives.

e.g.

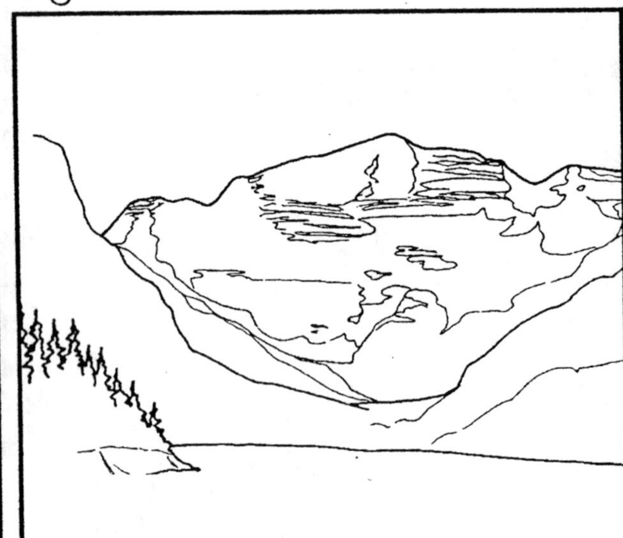

Front

Rocky Mountains

Dear David,
Having a great trip!
The Rockies are beautiful.
Love Mary

David Taylor
609 Apple Cres.
Winnipeg, Man.
Canada
R1H 7B3

Back

Choose a place that tourists like to visit.

Design a postcard for the place.

On your postcard **illustrate** a famous place.

CONSTABLE MACKENZIE'S READING

Activity One

Riddle Fun!

Read each riddle carefully.

Print the name of the province on the line provided.

1. This is a western province. It is the province between Saskatchewan and British Columbia. The capital city is Edmonton.
   The province is ________________________________

2. This is not a province. It lies between two other territories. Yellowknife is the capital city.
   The place is ________________________________ .

3. It is a western province. It is found between Manitoba and Alberta. Wheat is grown in this province.
   It is called ________________________________ .

4. This province is found on the west coast of Canada. Victoria ________________________________ is its capital city. Delicious apples and salmon are found here.
   It is the province called ________________________ .

5. It is Canada's largest province. Many people speak French here. Its capital city has the same name. Maple syrup comes ________________________________ from this province.
   It is called________________________________ .

6. It is an island and the smallest province in Canada. Potatoes grow well in its red dirt. Charlottetown is its capital city.
   It is called________________________________ .

CONSTABLE MACKENZIE'S READING

Activity One

7. It is found between Manitoba and Quebec. Its capital city is Toronto. Most of the people in Canada live here.

   It is called ______________________________.

8. It is a province made of two parts. Part of it is an island. Its capital city is called St. John's.

   It is called ______________________________.

9. It is the closest prairie province to Ontario. Buffalo used to roam over its land. Winnipeg is the capital city.

   It is called ______________________________.

10. It is an Atlantic province. It is a small province. Cape Breton Island is part of it. Its capital city is Halifax.

    It is called ______________________________.

11. Its capital city is Fredericton. It is found between Québec and Nova Scotia. There are many forests here. It is one of the Atlantic provinces. It is called ____________________.

12. It is the smallest territory. It became famous when gold was found here. Whitehorse is its capital city.

    It is called ______________________________.

13. It is a new territory. Many Inuit people live here. Its capital city is Iqaluit.

    It is called ______________________________.

CONSTABLE MACKENZIE'S READING

Activity Two

Have you ever seen?

Complete each rhyme with the correct pair of rhyming words

1. Have you ever seen a polar _______________ ,
   Eating a prickly _______________________?

2. Have you ever seen a silly ______________ ,
   Trying to eat crayfish with a _____________?

3. Have you ever seen a Canadian __________ ,
   Chop down a tree with a sharp ____________?

4. Have you ever seen a musk _______________ ,
   Wearing woolly pink ____________________?

5. Have you ever seen a mountain ___________ ,
   Floating on a river in a row ______________?

6. Have you ever seen a stinky ______________ ,
   Make his home in an old _______________?

7. Have you ever seen a ____________________ ,
   Travelling with a Canadian ______________?

8. Have you ever seen a _____________________,
   Driving a big logging _____________________?

woodchuck
socks
boat
skunk
truck
moose
bear
spoon
ox
goat
trunk
goose
beaver
pear
raccoon
cleaver

CONSTABLE MACKENZIE'S READING

Information Card One

Niagara Falls

Niagara Falls is one of the most spectacular natural wonders of North America. It is located in the province of Ontario. The falls are made of three waterfalls. They are called the Horseshoe Falls, the American Falls and the Bridal Veil Falls. The Horseshoe Falls is found in Ontario while the American Falls and the Bridal Veil Falls are found in the United States. The Horseshoe Falls is the largest and most beautiful. Canada has the best view of all the falls.

The water at the falls plunges into a steep gorge. The gorge is about 61 metres (200 feet) deep. You can hear the thundering roar of the falls well before you see them.

Niagara Falls attracts visitors from all over the world especially during the summer months. Sight-seeing steamers named "Maid of the Mist" take visitors close to the churning waters at the bottom of the falls. There is another trip you can take by walking under the falls with a guide. For both trips you must wear rain hats and raincoats so you won't get wet from the mist. At night the falls are colourfully lit with spotlights and are beautiful to see.

CONSTABLE MACKENZIE'S READING

Information Card One continued

Many years ago Native People living in the area used to throw beautiful maidens over the falls as a sacrifice. Many daredevils have tried to go over the falls in a barrel. Some were lucky to survive while others were killed. The first person to go over the Horseshoe Falls in a barrel was Anne Taylor, a sixty-three year old teacher, in 1901. She survived the dangerous trip and lived to talk about it. Many others have tried the same stunt but only a few have lived to tell about it. Some daredevils have even tried walking tightropes across it.

CONSTABLE MACKENZIE'S READING

Activity Three

Read Constable Mackenzie's Information Card called "**Niagara Falls**".

Read each sentence below carefully. Print **true** or **false** on the line at the beginning of each one.

_________ 1. All three falls are found in Canada.

_________ 2. The Horseshoe Falls is the largest and it is found in Ontario.

_________ 3. The falls make a loud thundering roar.

_________ 4. The Maid of the Mist is a steamer that takes you close to the falls.

_________ 5. Many years ago Indian Braves were thrown over the falls as a sacrifice.

_________ 6. All the people who have tried to go over the falls in a barrel have been killed.

_________ 7. The first daredevil to go over the falls was a teacher named Anne Taylor.

_________ 8. Niagara Falls is made of one big waterfall.

CONSTABLE MACKENZIE'S READING

Information Card Two

The Capilano Suspension Bridge

The world's greatest suspension footbridge is the Capilano Suspension Bridge found in Vancouver, British Columbia. The bridge is 135 metres (450 feet) long and 69 metres (230 feet) above the Capilano River.

It was built one hundred years ago by George Grant MacKay and two native men - August Jack and Willie Khahtsahlano. A team of horses helped to stretch the first hemp rope and cedar plank footbridge taut across the river. Many visitors came to visit the bridge to walk across it to the other side and to feel its swaying motion. Three more bridges were built later. Each one was built stronger and bigger than the one before it.

Today the area around the bridge is a park. At the park are a Trading Post and places to buy food. There are also many totem poles that were carved by local natives many years ago. These poles have been carefully looked after and preserved.

If you ever visit Vancouver be sure to visit the Capilano Suspension Bridge and Park.

CONSTABLE MACKENZIE'S READING 

Activity Four

Read Constable Mackenzie's Information Card called "**The Capilano Suspension Bridge**".

Answer each question in a complete sentence.

1. Where in Canada would you find the Capilano Suspension Bridge?

____

____

2. How long is the bridge?

____

____

3. Who built the first Capilano Suspension Bridge?

____

____

4. What did they use to build the first bridge?

____

____

5. What are the three things you would find at the park today?

____

____

____

____

CONSTABLE MACKENZIE'S READING

Information Card Three

The Calgary Stampede

The Calgary Stampede is held every year in July in Calgary's Stampede Park. It is a very large rodeo where cowboys compete in a variety of competitions for prize money. The Stampede lasts for ten days and everyone in the city becomes involved with all the fun. People dress up in western style clothes. The stores and restaurants are decorated with bales of hay and western decorations.

During the Stampede cowboys enter contests such as calf roping, riding bucking broncos and bulls, barrel racing, roping contests and chuckwagon racing. Funny clowns run about the ring trying to make the wild bulls go after them and not the cowboys who have fallen to the ground.

The audience is also entertained with a western musical grandstand show and the Royal Canadian Mounted Police Musical Ride.

The Calgary people welcome tourists and guests with their western friendliness to this wonderful celebration and their safe, clean city.

CONSTABLE MACKENZIE'S READING

Activity Five

Read Constable Mackenzie's Information card called "**The Calgary Stampede**".

Can you match the beginning of the sentence to its correct ending?

1. The Calgary Stampede is held ..	_____ large rodeo for cowboys.
2. The Stampede is a	_____ lasts for ten days.
3. The Calgary Stampede.....	_____ for prize money.
4. Everyone in Calgary	_____ and ride bucking broncos.
5. The cowboys compete	_____ dresses up in western clothes.
6. Cowboys rope calves	_____ friendly, safe, clean city.
7. Funny clowns act silly to	_____ every July in Calgary's Stampede Park.
8. The people of Calgary are proud of their	_____ try to fool the bucking bulls and horses.

CONSTABLE MACKENZIE'S READING

Information Card Four

The Fortress of Louisbourg

The Fortress of Louisbourg is located on Cape Breton Island in Nova Scotia. It is a wonderful place where you can see some of the history of Canada. Many tourists visit it every year. It is called a fortress rather than a fort because it is a town and a military base surrounded by a wall.

Louisbourg was built by the French about three hundred years ago. It was built to prevent the English from taking their land and possessions.

Two battles between the English and the French took place at Louisbourg. The English won both battles. After the first battle the fortress was given back to the French but two years after the second one, Louisbourg was destroyed by the English.

For two hundred years the fortress lay in ruins. In 1928, the government of Canada decided to make it a historic site and had its ruins rebuilt.

Today when you walk through the fortress' gates you will be stopped by a sentry on duty. He will question you in French or English and then let you pass.

Once you are past the gates you will travel back in time. Everyone will be dressed in costumes as rich people, poor people and soldiers. You will be able to visit fifty different homes and buildings.

CONSTABLE MACKENZIE'S READING

Information Card Four continued

The people will surprise and entertain you with their stories, songs, dances, music, cooking, sewing and many more activities. The soldiers will answer any questions that you ask about life at Louisbourg. You may watch a military drill or hear muskets firing and the sound of drums beating.

If you ever visit Cape Breton Island, be sure to stop at Louisbourg. I'm sure you will enjoy every minute of your step back in time.

CONSTABLE MACKENZIE'S READING

Activity Six

Read Constable Mackenzie's Information Card called "**The Fortress of Louisbourg**".

A) Look for a word in the story that means the same as each word below.

1. visitors ______________________
2. past ______________________
3. belongings ______________________
4. made over ______________________
5. fights ______________________
6. ruined ______________________
7. guard ______________________
8. clothes ______________________
9. old guns ______________________

B) How many syllables do you hear in each word below?

1. Louisbourg _____
2. fortress _____
3. fort _____
4. battles _____
5. history _____
6. costumes _____
7. wonderful _____
8. musket _____

CONSTABLE MACKENZIE'S READING

Information Card Five

Covered Bridges

In the province of New Brunswick you will find seventy covered bridges. These bridges were often called "Kissing" bridges. Many years ago young people who were courting would stop their horse-drawn buggies on the covered bridges where it was dark and private to steal a kiss or two.

These bridges looked like long barn-like buildings over rivers and large streams. They were built to help people travel from one side of the river to the other. The bridge provided a safe way to cross a river, and the roof and walls protected the bridge from our Canadian winters and prevented it from rotting as fast.

Horses found it difficult to keep a firm grip with their hooves and often slid about on the bridges when they were icy or snowy. Sometimes a horse would become frightened when it heard the sound of the rushing water while crossing the bridge, and it would try to run away.

The world's longest covered bridge is found in a small farming town called Hartland in New Brunswick. The Hartland Covered Bridge is 391 metres long (1 282 feet) and it crosses the Saint John River.

CONSTABLE MACKENZIE'S READING

Activity Seven

Read Constable Mackenzie's Information Card called "**Covered Bridges**"

Complete each sentence below with the correct word or words found in the box at the bottom of the page.

1. There are ____________ covered bridges in ______________.
2. ______________ bridges were often called ________________ bridges.
3. A covered ______________ looked like a long ____________ over a ____.
4. The ________________ and _______________ protected the bridge from ____.
5. The bridges were __________ for horses to cross in the winter.
6. The sound of the ___________________ water under a bridge often ____________ a horse causing it to ___________ away.
7. People used the bridge to ______________ from one side to the other.
8. The ______________ covered bridge in the world is found in ____.

Hartland	**rushing**	**travel**
frightened	**longest**	**run**
dangerous	**winter**	**walls**
covered	**rotting**	**roof**
seventy	**river**	**barn**
New Brunswick	**kissing**	**bridge**

CONSTABLE MACKENZIE'S READING

Information Card Six

Canada's Far North

Many people think the ideal holiday is travelling to Canada's far north. Here they can get away from people and be in a place where the scenery is beautiful.

Canada's far north is filled with mountains, wilderness country, deep canyons, and icebergs as tall as city buildings. During the summer the tundra is coloured by miniature bright flowers, taiga and boreal forests. The rivers are crystal clear and are filled with rushing white water which excite and thrill any visitor.

Huge herds of bison, elk and caribou can be seen grazing on the tundra. In the mountain wilderness country, lynx, Dall sheep, Arctic and red wolves, black bears, grizzly bears, polar bears and musk oxen can be seen hunting for food.

The best time to visit Canada's great northern territories is in the months of June, July, August and early September. The days are long and in the middle of summer it is light all day long.

Tourists travel about by airplane, boat, canoe, raft, helicopter and bus to see the amazing sights in Canada's far north. In some areas there are very few hotels and gas stations between towns.

A trip to Canada's far north would be very exciting indeed.

CONSTABLE MACKENZIE'S READING

Activity Eight

Read Constable Mackenzie's Information card called **"Canada's Far North"**.

Complete the following activities.

1. Make a list of animals a visitor may see in Canada's far north.

____

____

____

____

____

____

____

____

2. Illustrate a picture of "Canada's far north".

IONA INUIT'S MATHEMATICS

Activity One

Place Value Fun!

A) What is the place value of each number?

Numeral	Thousands	Hundreds	Tens	Ones
1. 5632	______	______	______	______
2. 733	______	______	______	______
3. 2 063	______	______	______	______
4. 9 980	______	______	______	______
5. 607	______	______	______	______
6. 1 851	______	______	______	______
7. 3 954	______	______	______	______
8. 273	______	______	______	______

B) What is the place value of each circled numeral?

1. 5 (6) 2 7 ______________________

2. 9 0 7 (1) ______________________

3. (8) 7 4 3 ______________________

4. 2 6 (9) 5 ______________________

IONA INUIT'S MATHEMATICS

Activity Two

Expanding Numerals

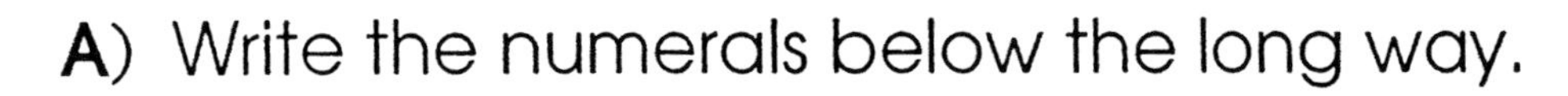

A) Write the numerals below the long way.

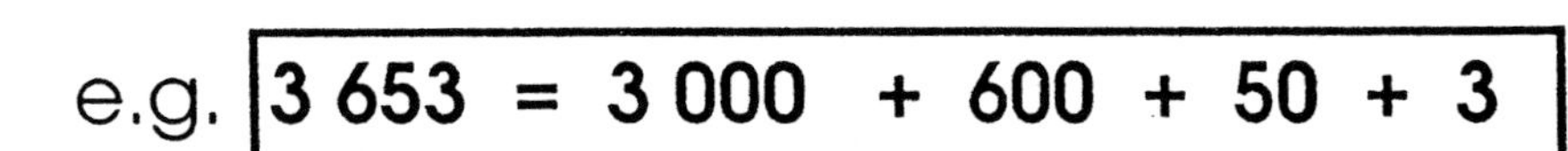

e.g. **3 653 = 3 000 + 600 + 50 + 3**

1. 5 095 = ________ + ________ + ________ + ________
2. 9 786 = ________ + ________ + ________ + ________
3. 653 = ________ + ________ + ________ + ________
4. 8 002 = ________ + ________ + ________ + ________
5. 7 504 = ________ + ________ + ________ + ________
6. 2 065 = ________ + ________ + ________ + ________
7. 1 111 = ________ + ________ + ________ + ________
8. 6 731 = ________ + ________ + ________ + ________
9. 956 = ________ + ________ + ________ + ________
10. 3 605 = ________ + ________ + ________ + ________

B) Write the numeral that comes next.

1. 5 631, ______________
2. 760, ______________
3. 8 069, ______________
4. 7 213, ______________
5. 5 000, ______________
6. 4 999, ______________
7. 6 339, ______________
8. 889, ______________

IONA INUIT'S MATHEMATICS

Activity Three

Writing Numerals the Short Way

A) **Collect** the numerals to write one big numeral.

1. 1 000 + 500 + 60 + 1 = ____________________
2. 2 000 + 70 + 5 = ____________________
3. 600 + 60 + 6 = ____________________
4. 9 000 + 900 + 90 + 9 = ____________________
5. 5 000 + 1 = ____________________
6. 3 000 + 60 + 3 = ____________________
7. 800 + 90 + 6 = ____________________
8. 7 000 + 900 + 50 + 3 = ____________________

B) **Count by 1's**. Fill in the missing numerals.

1. 4 563, __________, __________, __________, __________
2. 2 019, __________, __________, __________, __________
3. 3 459, __________, __________, __________, __________
4. 681, __________, __________, __________, __________
5. 1 001, __________, __________, __________, __________
6. 6 781, __________, __________, __________, __________

IONA INUIT'S MATHEMATICS

Activity Four

Reading and Writing Numerals

A) Write the following number words as numerals.

1. five hundred forty-one ____________
2. one thousand fifty-one ____________
3. eight hundred seventy-three ____________
4. five hundred thirteen ____________
5. six thousand one hundred and two ____________
6. eleven hundred and two ____________
7. four thousand nine hundred six ____________
8. one thousand five hundred eleven ____________
9. three thousand two hundred ____________
10. nine thousand seven hundred forty ____________

B) Print the numeral that comes before and after.

1. ________ 9 631 ________
2. ________ 3 260 ________
3. ________ 2 003 ________
4. ________ 699 ________
5. ________ 8 019 ________
6. ________ 6 000 ________
7. ________ 710 ________
8. ________ 7 613 ________

IONA INUIT'S MATHEMATICS

Activity Five

Writing Numerals as Number Words

A) Write each numeral below as a number word.

1. 505 - ______________________________
2. 1 673 - ______________________________
3. 5 640 - ______________________________
4. 2 531 - ______________________________
5. 3 030 - ______________________________
6. 4 871 - ______________________________
7. 699 - ______________________________
8. 9 380 - ______________________________

B) Is the first numeral greater than (>) or less than (<) the second numeral?

1.	5 6 33	______	1 642	6.	7 031	______	8 431
2.	660	______	6 660	7.	1 602	______	6 102
3.	540	______	249	8.	7 654	______	7 649
4.	1 112	______	112	9.	2 131	______	2 013
5.	1 231	______	1 321	10.	996	______	9 966

Let's Visit Canada
Name:

Canada

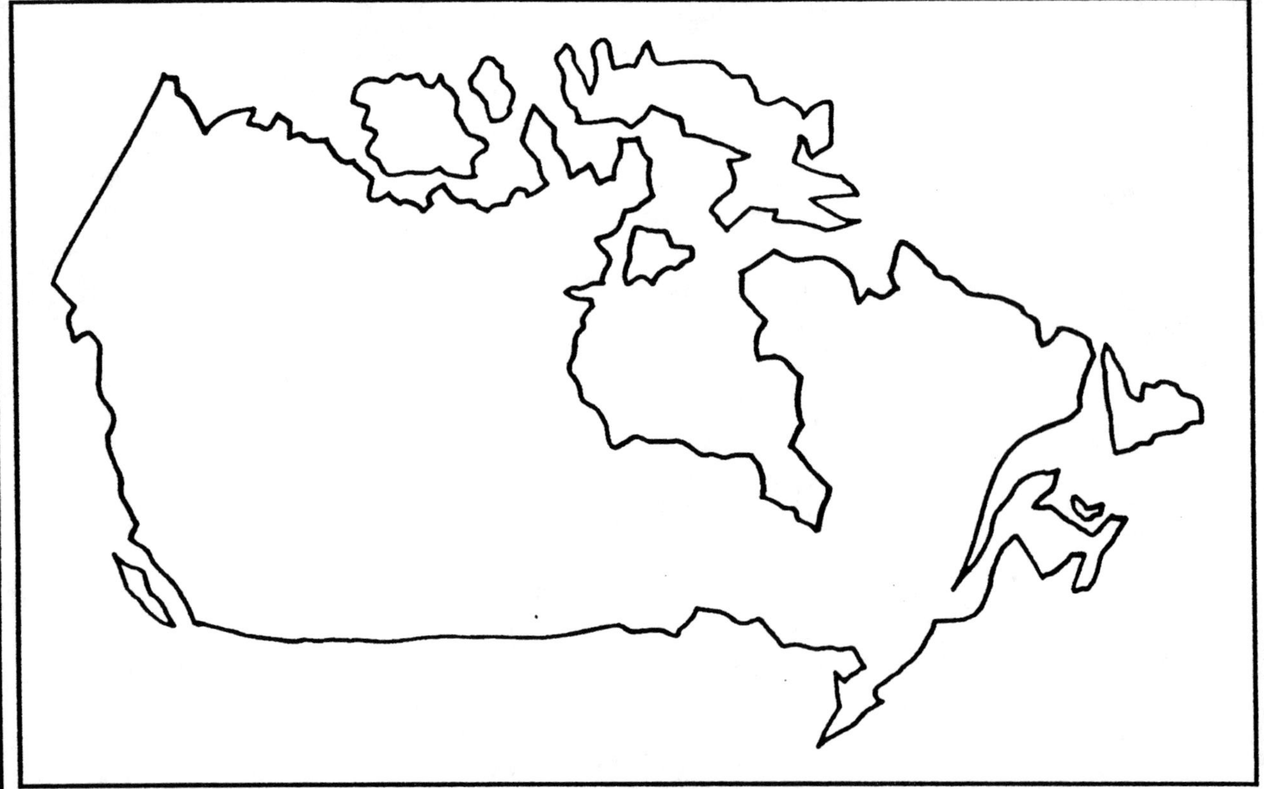

Canada is a big ______________ found in ______________________

______________. The word "Canada" comes from a native word

that means ____.

Canada is the ___________________ largest country in the world.

Its closest neighbour is the _________________ _________________.

The ________________ ______________ is found on the East Coast.

The ________________ _______________ is found on the West Coast.

The ______________ ______________ is found on the Northern Coast.

Page One

Canada

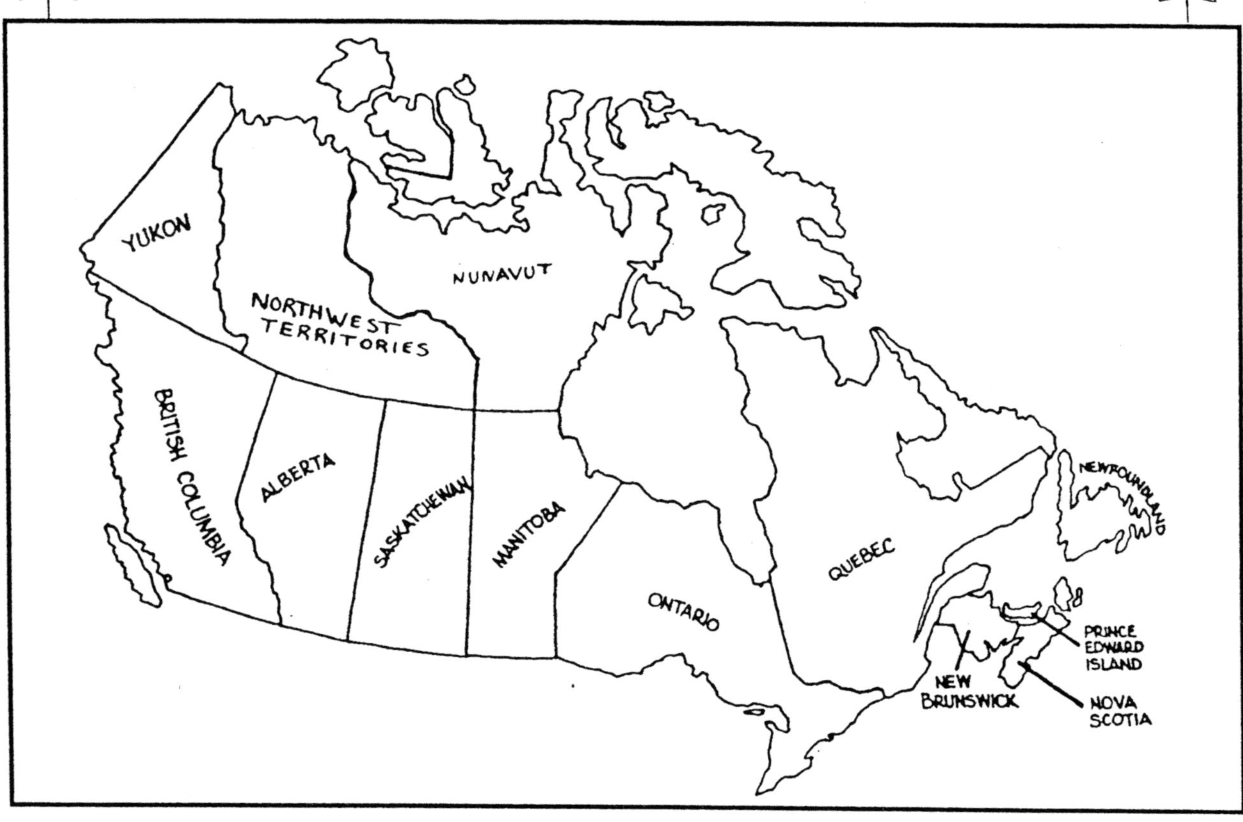

Canada is divided into ten ____________________ and three ____.

Most of Canada's ____________________ people live in Nunavut.

The capital city of Canada is _______________. It is located in the province of _______________. The Prime Minister of Canada is ____________________. He/She is the leader of Canada's ______________________________.

Canada's national anthem is called _____________. Canada's national motto is " A Mari Usque ad Mari" which means from

____________ ____________ ____________ ____________.

Colour each province and territory a different colour. Colour the oceans blue.

Page Two

Parts of Canada

Canada is divided into ________ provinces and ________ territories.

Each province and territory has a capital city.

On the chart below list the provinces, territories and their capital cities.

Provinces	
Name of Province	**Capital City**
1. ________	________
2. ________	________
3. ________	________
4. ________	________
5. ________	________
6. ________	________
7. ________	________
8. ________	________
9. ________	________
10. ________	________

Territories	
Name of Territory	**Capital City**
1. ________	________
2. ________	________
3. ________	________

Page Three

Provinces and Territories

Québec

Canada is divided into _______________ and _______________. The largest province is _______________. The people in Québec speak mainly _______________. Québec has two large cities - _______________ and _______________. The main industry in Québec is _______________.

_______________ is Canada's second largest province in size. More than _______________ of the people living in Canada live in Ontario. _______________ and _______________ are the two main cities. Ottawa is the capital city of all of Canada. Toronto is the capital city of Ontario. Ontario's main industry is making _______________.

Provinces and Territories

The Western provinces are ______________ ______________, ________________________and ________________. In Manitoba and Saskatchewan there are very large ________________ and the farmers grow ________________. In Alberta there are many ______________ ______________. British Columbia is filled with many large ______________ that are cut down for ________________.

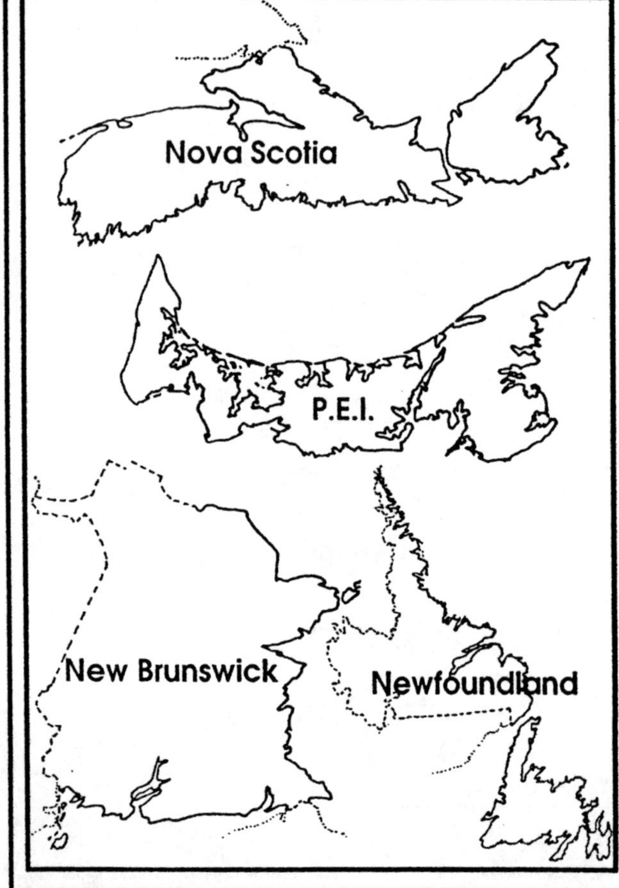

The Atlantic Provinces are found on the ______________ coast of Canada. They are ________________________, ________________________, ________________________ and ________________________.

The ______________ province in Canada is Prince Edward Island. ______________ is an important industry in these provinces. Many tourists visit the Atlantic Provinces every year to see all the beautiful scenery and historical places.

Provinces and Territories

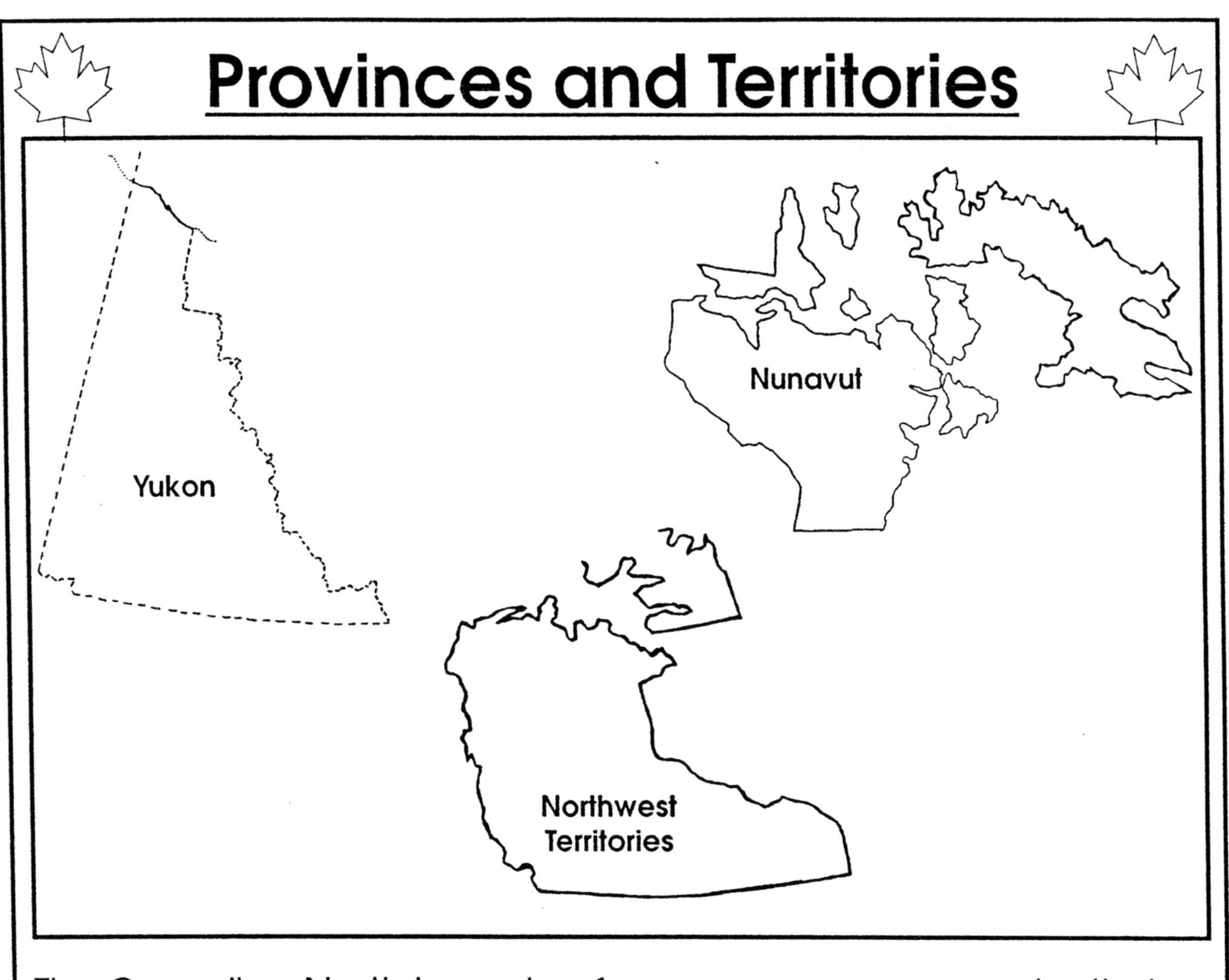

The Canadian North is made of ____________________ territories. They are the ____________________, ____________________ ______________, and ______________. Nunavut is a __________ territory where many of Canada's ____________ people live. The ____________________ live mainly in the Northwest Territories. Canada's northland is ______________ and ______________. The main industries here are ________________, ________________ and ____________________. The people depend on large boats and planes to bring in their supplies. Travelling from place to place is done by special land vehicles. Airplanes, boats, snowmobiles and dog sleds are still used.

Page Six

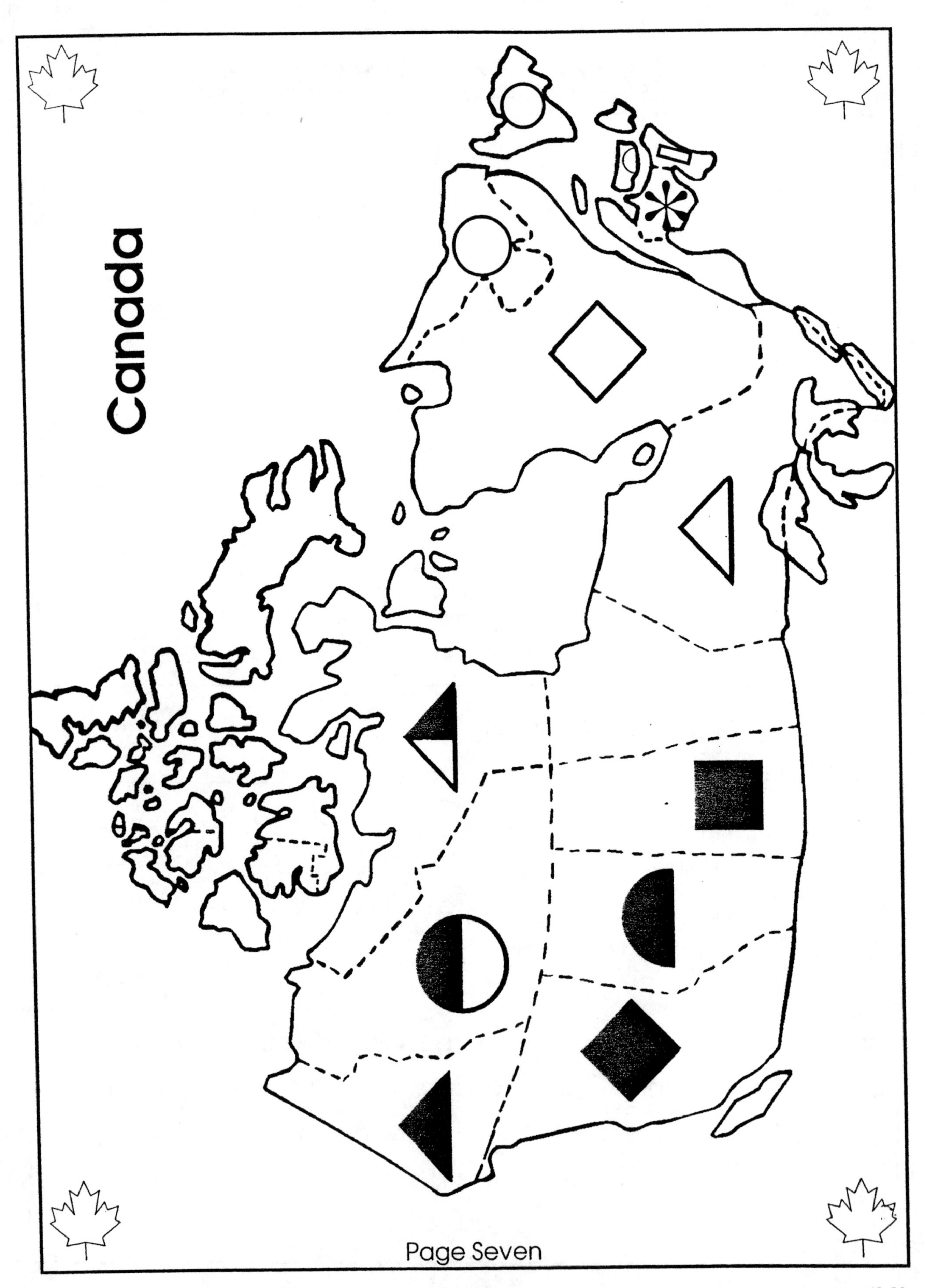

Page Seven

Map of Canada

Look at the map of Canada.

Find the province in which you live. **Colour** it red.

Match the shape on the province to its name. **Complete** the chart below.

Symbol	Province or Territory
1. ○	______
2. (outlined semicircle)	______
3. *	______
4. ▭	______
5. ◇	______
6. △	______
7. ●	______
8. ■	______
9. (filled semicircle)	______
10. ◆	______
11. ▲	______
12. (circle, top half filled)	______
13. (triangle, right half filled)	______

Page Eight

The Canadian Flag

The Canadian Flag is a ____________ emblem. It is ____________ and ________________ in colour. In the centre of the flag on a white background is a red _______________ _______________. The maple leaf has _______________ points. Each point represents a _________________ and the _________________ _________________. The red colour stands for _________________ and the white colour stands for _________________. Canada's flag became our official flag on _________________________. Canada's earlier flag was the _______________ _______________, which is the flag that represents England.

Page Nine

Canada's Capital City

Ottawa

Ottawa is the ______________ city of Canada. It is found in the province of ______________ on the ______________ ______________.

The ______________ ______________ are located on Parliament Hill in Ottawa. Many people who live in Ottawa work for the ______________. The ______________ ______________ and other ______________________ live and work in Ottawa too. They make ______________________ and plans for the country.

In Ottawa there is a famous canal called the ______________ ______________. In the winter, people like to ______________ on it during a celebration called ______________________. In the spring, tourists come to Ottawa for the ______________ ______________. At that time of the year Ottawa is quite colourful.

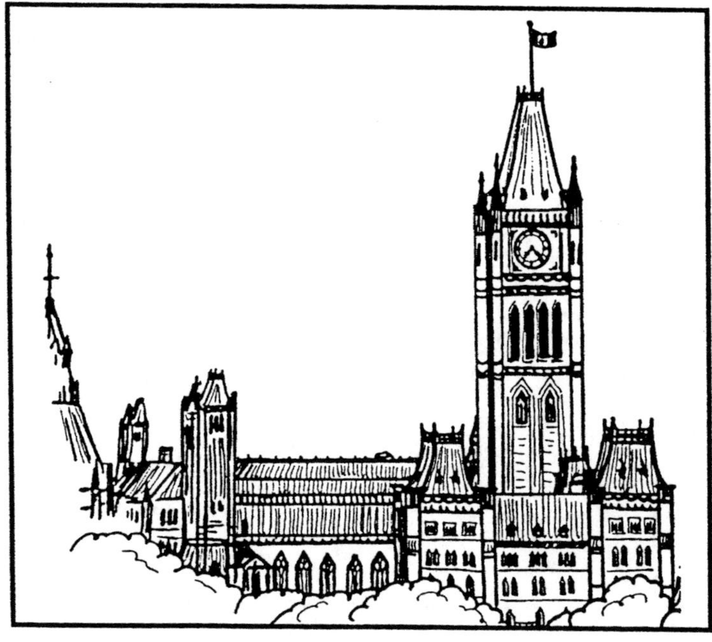

Page Ten

Provincial and Territorial Flags

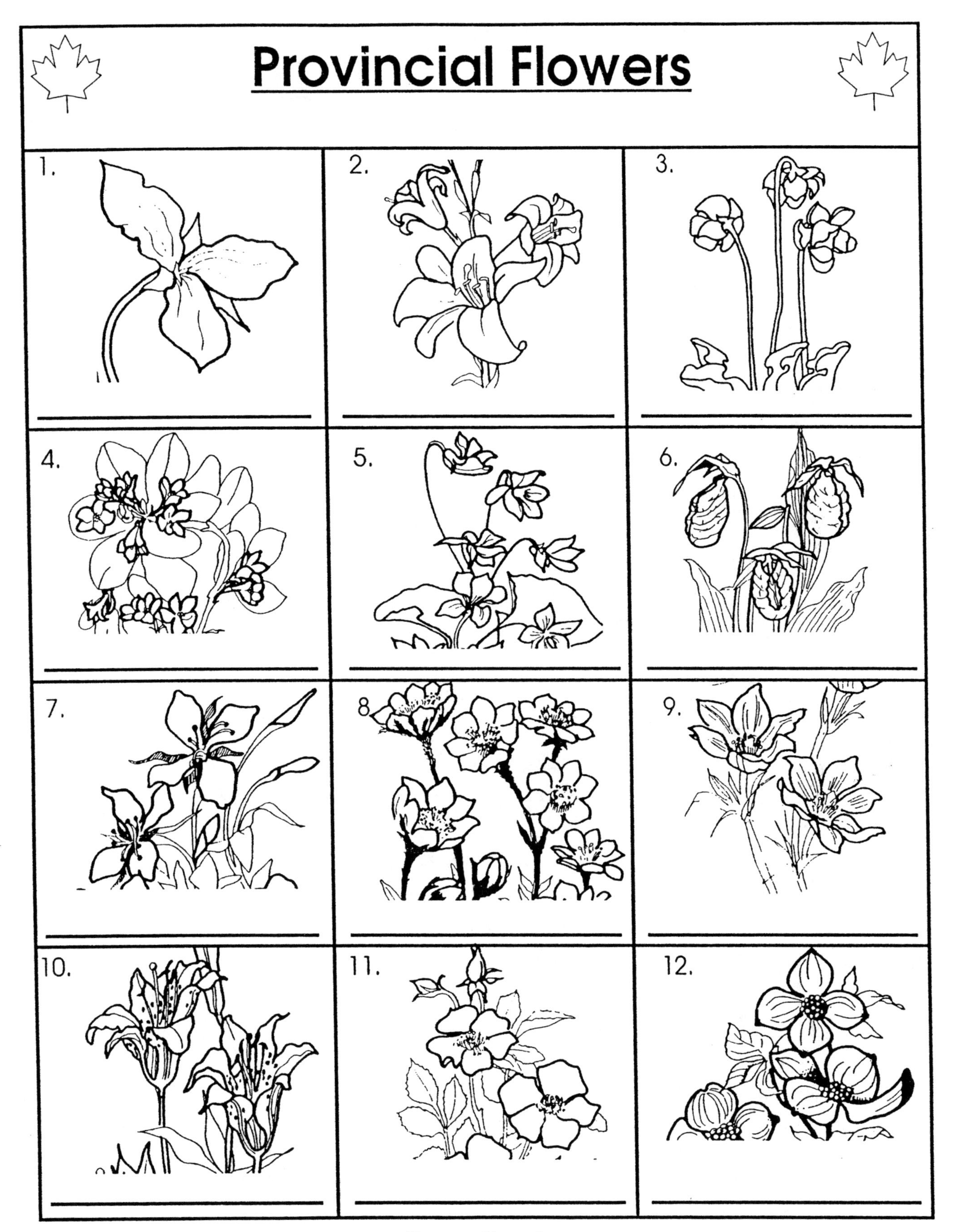

Page Twelve

Let's Visit Canada

Answer Keys

Maxine Maple Leaf's Sounds #1:
1. groundhogs; fields 2. Oceans 3. deer; heads 4. Moose; feed 5. three; bears 6. prairies;fields; wheat 7. goose; south 8. bear; food; seal 9. Raccoons; raid; pails 10. beaver; teeth; trees

Maxine Maple Leaf's Sounds #2:
1. sk 2. gr 3. sn 4. fl 5. pr 6. pr 7. Fr 8. pr 9. gr 10. sk 11. gl 12. sn

Maxine Maple Leaf's Sounds #3:
1. cable 2. table 3. fable 4. stable 5. ladle 6. cradle 7. rattle 8. paddle 9. cattle 10. twinkle

Maxine Maple Leaf's Sounds #4:
1. bb 2. mm 3. tt 5. nn 6. ll 7. rr 8. rr 9. ss 10. cc 11. ll 12. mm 13. ll 14. ff

Maxine Maple Leaf's Sounds #5:
Hard "C Words: Calgary, corn, community, canal, capital, caribou
Soft "C" Words: city, mice, place, ice, space, rice

Maxine Maple Leaf's Sounds #6:
1. p ⓞ l ~~a~~ r b ⓔ ~~a~~ r (Long o, short e)
2. p ⓞ r c ⓤ p ⓘ n ~~e~~ (long o, short u, long i)
3. c h ⓘ p m ⓤ n k (short i, short u)
4. p r ⓞ v ⓘ n c ~~e~~ (short o, short i)
5. m ⓐ p l ~~e~~ s y r ⓤ p (long a, short u)
6. t ⓞ t ⓔ m p ⓞ l ~~e~~ (long o, short e, long o)
7. M ⓐ n ⓘ t ⓞ b ⓐ (short a, short i, long o, short a)
8. N ⓤ n ⓐ v ⓤ t (short u, short a, short u)
9. v ⓘ l l ⓐ g ~~e~~ (short i, short a)
10. W h ⓘ t ~~e~~ h ⓞ r s ~~e~~ (long i, long o)

Maxine Maple Leaf's Sounds #7:
1. th, th 2. Th, wh 3. ch 4. ch 5. sh 6. wh, wh, th 7. wh 8. ch 9. ch, ch 10. ch

Louie Lumberjack's Word Study #1:
Amherst, Battleford, Calgary, Dauphin, Edmonton, Fredericton, Goderich, Hamilton, Inuvik, Kingston, London, Moncton, Neepawa, Ottawa, Pond Inlet, Quebec City, Regina, Saskatoon, Thunder Bay, Vancouver, Whitehorse, Yarmouth

Louie Lumberjack's Word Study #2:
1. maple leaves 2. territories 3. provinces 4. cities 5. moose 6. communities 7. deer 8. Canada Geese 9. Arctic Foxes 10. countries 11. oceans 12. walruses

Let's Visit Canada

Louie Lumberjack's Word Study #3:

1. (2) 2. (4) 3. (3) 4. (4) 5. (3) 6. (5) 7. (6) 8. (4) 9. (3) 10. (4) 11. (2) 12. (3) 13. (6)

Louie Lumberjack's Word Study #4:

1. groundhog 2. Charlottetown 3. neighbourhood 4. Whitehorse 5. Yellowknife 6. waterfalls 7. lumberjack 8. Newfoundland 9. evergreen 10. cowboys

Louie Lumberjack's Word Study #5:

Word Search

A N O R T H W E S T T E R R I T O R I E S
P O B Q A M V D C L K Z Q D J Y E A P F A
H V P C B R N U Q N U N A V U T O U Y B S
J A T A R D B E I W R D U X X N I G O H K
A S A K I S E B O O C S R N C B T G C A A
U C I B T D T F N B C A B S F E U Z Z H T
K O A L I J V L T G K H H T M C W B Q G C
Q T G C S I B L A U U V D T A T F M F H H
V I R M H W J A R J H M C I N S I C J R E
R A S Y C F N H I K E J E C I W G U D N W
T X Z P O I C Z O K G V E M T K F L V Y A
A Q I S L A Q G R Q S L Q D O N O D M O N
C U B B U X K C I W S N U R B W E N W P G
H E T Y M J O W J U S M R E A W O A V X P
V B D I B Y L P Y K D V X K U R P L F N L
A E B Z I T Z X J W K U E J Y F M D X Q Z
F C H E A C W M A L A L O V M W R N S J Y
A K B G X V S D H X L T N I S M N U N L P
E J Y U K O N Y D G B R H P Q G I O M O I
C G L F G B S E N Y E F R O K Q O F H T Z
V I Z W C A C Z T M R L P E Q O F W N P K
H Y D A M X U D B Z T E N S P R J E T U I
F P R I N C E E D W A R D I S L A N D O Q

Let's Visit Canada

Louie Lumberjack's Word Study #7:

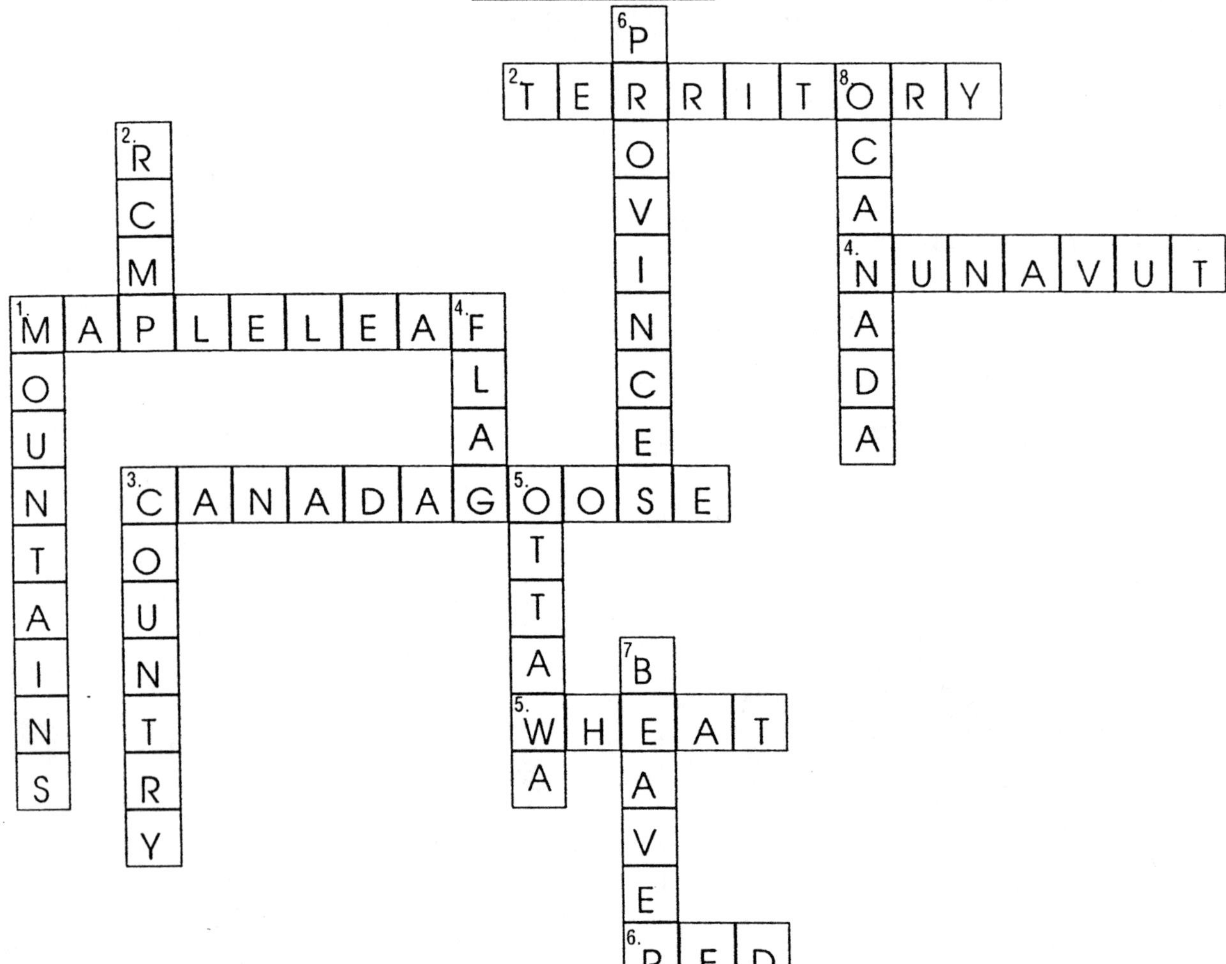

Lumberjack's Word Study #8:

1. ocean 2. lake 3. river 4. provinces 5. city 6. mountains 7. villages 8. country

Bonhomme's Brainstorming #7:

Forest Animals: squirrel, moose, wolf, skunk, raccoon, opossum, deer, chipmunk, fox, rabbit, black bear, porcupine, beaver

Tree Animals: squirrel, porcupine, raccoon, opossum

Water Animals: beaver, salmon, walrus, flounder, trout, muskrat

Air Animals: eagle, seagull, Canada Goose

Mountain Animals: mountain lion, mountain goat, grizzly bear, lynx

Cochrane Cowboy's Research #1:

1. (Answers will vary.) 2. Ontario 3. Prince Edward Island 4. Manitoba 5. French, English 6. Québec 7. Newfoundland, Nova Scotia, New Brunswick, Prince Edward Island 8. Prince Edward Island, Newfoundland 9. Manitoba, Saskatchewan, Alberta 10. Arctic Ocean 11. Atlantic Ocean 12. Yukon 13. Thirteen (10 provinces + 3 territories) 14. Pacific Ocean 15. Ottawa 16. Nunavut

Let's Visit Canada

Constable Mackenzie's Reading #1:
1. Alberta 2. Northwest Territories 3. Saskatchewan 4. British Columbia 5. Québec 6. Prince Edward Island 7. Ontario 8. Newfoundland 9. Manitoba 10. Nova Scotia 11. New Brunswick 12. Yukon 13. Nunavut

Constable Mackenzie's Reading #2:
1. bear, pear 2. raccoon, spoon 3. beaver, cleaver 4. ox, socks 5. goat, boat 6. skunk, trunk 7. moose, goose 8. woodchuck, truck

Constable Mackenzie's Reading #3:
1. False 2. True 3. True 4. True 5. False 6. False 7. True 8. False

Constable Mackenzie's Reading #4:
1. It is found in Vancouver, British Columbia.
2. The bridge is 135 metres long.
3. The first bridge was built by George Mackay, August Jack and Willie Khahtsahlano.
4. They used hemp rope and cedar planks.
5. You would find a Trading Post, places to buy food and old totem poles.

Constable Mackenzie's Reading #5:
2, 3, 5, 6, 4, 7, 8, 1

Constable Mackenzie's Reading #6:
A) 1. tourists 2. history 3. possessions 4. rebuilt 5. battles 6. destroyed 7. sentry 8. costumes 9. muskets

B) 1. (3) 2. (2) 3. (1) 4. (2) 5. (3) 6. (2) 7. (3) 8. (2)

Constable Mackenzie's Reading #7:
1. seventy, New Brunswick 2. Covered, Kissing 3. bridge, barn, river 4. roof, walls, rotting 5. dangerous, river 6. rushing, frightened, run 7. travel 8. longest, Hartland

Constable Mackenzie's Reading #8:
1. bison, Dall sheep, black bears, elk, Arctic wolves, grizzly bears, caribou, red wolves, Polar bears, lynx, mountain sheep, musk oxen
2. Answers will vary.

Iona's Inuit's Mathematics #1:
A) 1. 5TH, 6H, 3T, 2O
2. 7H, 3T, 3O
3. 2TH, 0H, 6T, 3O
4. 9TH, 9H, 9T, 0O
5. 6H, 0T, 7O
6. 1TH, 8H, 5T, 1O
7. 3TH, 9H, 5T, 4O
8. 2H, 7T, 3O

B) 1. Hundreds 2. Ones 3. Thousands 4. Tens

Let's Visit Canada

Iona Inuit's Mathematics #2:

A) 1. 5 000 + 0 + 90 + 5
2. 9 000 + 700 + 80 + 6
3. 600 + 50 + 3
4. 8 000 + 0 + 0 + 2
5. 7 000 + 500 + 0 + 4
6. 2 000 + 0 + 60 + 5
7. 1 000 + 100 + 10 + 1
8. 6 000 + 700 + 30 + 1
9. 900 + 50 + 6
10. 3 000 + 600 + 0 + 5

B) a) 5 632 b) 761 c) 8070 d) 7 214 e) 5 001 f) 5 000 g) 6 340 h) 890

Iona Inuit's Mathematics #3:

A) 1. 1 561 2. 2 073 3. 666 4. 9 999 5. 5 001 6. 3 063 7. 896 8. 7 95s

B) 1. 4 564, 4 565, 4 566, 4 567
2. 2 020, 2 021, 2 022, 2023
3. 3 460, 3 461, 3 462, 3 463
4. 682, 683, 684, 685
5. 1 002, 1 003, 1 004, 1 005
6. 6 782, 6 783, 6,784, 6 785

Iona Inuit's Mathematics #4:

A) 1. 541 2. 1 051 3. 873 4. 513 5. 6 102 6. 1 102 7. 4 906 8. 1 511 9. 3 200 10. 9 740

B) a) 9 630, 9 632 b) 3 259, 3 260 c) 2 002, 2 004 d) 698, 700 e) 8 013, 8 015
f) 5 999, 6 001
g) 709, 711 h) 7 612, 7 614

Iona Inuit's Mathematics #5:

A) 1. five hundred five
2. one thousand, six hundred, seventy-three
3. five thousand, six hundred, forty
4. two thousand, five hundred, thirty-one
5. three thousand, thirty
6. four thousand, eight hundred, seventy-one
7. six hundred, ninety-nine
8. nine thousand, three hundred, eighty

B) 1. > 2. < 3. > 4. > 5. < 6. < 7. < 8. > 9. > 10. <

Reproducible Student Booklet

Page One: Canada

country; North America; village; second; United States; Atlantic Ocean; Pacific Ocean; Arctic Ocean

Page Two: Canada

provinces; territories; Inuit; Ottawa; Ontario; Present One; government; O Canada; sea to sea

Let's Visit Canada

Page Three: Parts of Canada

Provinces:

1. Newfoundland	St. John's
2. Nova Scotia	Halifax
3. New Brunswick	Fredericton
4. Prince Edward Island	Charlottetown
5. Québec	Québec City
6. Ontario	Toronto
7. Manitoba	Winnipeg
8. Saskatchewan	Regina
9. Alberta	Edmonton
10. British Columbia	Victoria

Territories

1. Northwest Territories	Yellowknife
2. The Yukon	Whitehorse
3. Nunavut	Iqaluit

Page Four: Provinces and Territories

provinces; territories; Québec; French; Montreal; Québec City; forestry
Ontario; one-third; Ottawa; Toronto; automobiles

Page Five: Provinces and Territories

Manitoba; Saskatchewan; Alberta; British Columbia; farms; wheat; cattle ranches; trees; lumber; east; Newfoundland; Nova Scotia; New Brunswick; Prince Edward Island; smallest; Fishing

Page Six: provinces and Territories

three; Yukon: Northwest Territories; Nunavut; Inuit; Dene; cold; barren; mining; hunting; trapping

Page Eight: Map of Canada

1. Newfoundland 2. Prince Edward Island 3. New Brunswick 4. Nova Scotia 5. Québec 6. Ontario 7. Manitoba 8. Saskatchewan 9. Alberta 10. British Columbia 11. Yukon 12. Northwest Territories 13. Nunavut

Page Nine: The Canadian Flag

national; red; white; maple leaf; eleven; province; three; territories; strength; purity; February 15, 1965; Union Jack

Page Ten: Ottawa

capital; Ontario; Ottawa River; Parliament Buildings; government; Prime Minister; politicians; laws; Rideau Canal; skate; Winter Interlude; Tulip Festival

Page Eleven: Provincial and Territorial Flags

1. Ontario 2. Québec 3. Nova Scotia 4. Prince Edward Island 5. Newfoundland 6. New Brunswick 7. Manitoba 8. Saskatchewan 9. British Columbia 10. Alberta 11. Yukon 12. Northwest Territories 13. Nunavut

Page Twelve: Provincial Flowers

1. Trillium 2. Madonna Lily 3. Pitcher Plant 4. Mayflower 5. Purple Violet 6. Lady's Slipper 7. Fireweed 8. Mountain Avens 9. Prairie Crocus 10. Red Lily 11. Wild Rose 12. Pacific Dogwood

Use the reproducible pictures to decorate other activity cards that you may want to make to add to the theme on Canada

Publication Listing

Code #	Title and Grade
SSC1-12	A Time of Plenty Gr. 2
SSN1-92	Abel's Island NS Gr. 4-6
SSF1-16	Aboriginal Peoples of Canada Gr. 7-8
SSK1-31	Addition & Subtraction Drills Gr. 1-3
SSK1-28	Addition Drills Gr. 1-3
SSY1-04	Addition Gr. 1-3
SSN1-174	Adv. of Huckle Berry Finn NS Gr. 7-8
SSB1-63	African Animals Gr 4-6
SSB1-29	All About Bears Gr. 1-2
SSF1-08	All About Boats Gr. 2-3
SSJ1-02	All About Canada Gr. 2
SSB1-54	All About Cattle Gr. 4-6
SSN1-10	All About Colours Gr. P-1
SSB1-93	All About Dinosaurs Gr. 2
SSN1-14	All About Dragons Gr. 3-5
SSB1-07	All About Elephants Gr. 3-4
SSB1-68	All About Fish Gr. 4-6
SSN1-39	All About Giants Gr. 2-3
SSH1-15	All About Jobs Gr. 1-3
SSH1-05	All About Me Gr. 1
SSA1-02	All About Mexico Gr. 4-6
SSR1-28	All About Nouns Gr. 5-7
SSF1-09	All About Planes Gr. 2-3
SSB1-33	All About Plants Gr. 2-3
SSR1-29	All About Pronouns Gr. 5-7
SSB1-12	All About Rabbits Gr. 2-3
SSB1-58	All About Spiders Gr. 4-6
SSA1-03	All About the Desert Gr. 4-6
SSA1-04	All About the Ocean Gr. 5-7
SSZ1-01	All About the Olympics Gr. 2-4
SSB1-49	All About the Sea Gr. 4-6
SSK1-06	All About Time Gr. 4-6
SSF1-07	All About Trains Gr. 2-3
SSH1-18	All About Transportation Gr. 2
SSB1-01	All About Trees Gr. 4-6
SSB1-61	All About Weather Gr. 7-8
SSB1-06	All About Whales Gr. 3-4
SSPC-26	All Kinds of Clocks B/W Pictures
SSB1-110	All Kinds of Structures Gr. 1
SSH1-19	All Kinds of Vehicles Gr. 3
SSF1-01	Amazing Aztecs Gr. 4-6
SSB1-92	Amazing Earthworms Gr. 2-3
SSJ1-50	Amazing Facts in Cdn History Gr. 4-6
SSB1-32	Amazing Insects Gr. 4-6
SSN1-132	Amelia Bedelia–Camping NS 1-3
SSN1-68	Amelia Bedelia NS 1-3
SSN1-155	Amelia Bedelia-Surprise Shower NS 1-3
SSA1-13	America The Beautiful Gr. 4-6
SSN1-57	Amish Adventure NS 7-8
SSF1-02	Ancient China Gr. 4-6
SSF1-18	Ancient Egypt Gr. 4-6
SSF1-21	Ancient Greece Gr. 4-6
SSF1-19	Ancient Rome Gr. 4-6
SSQ1-06	Animal Town – Big Book Pkg 1-3
SSQ1-02	Animals Prepare Winter – Big Book Pkg 1-3
SSN1-150	Animorphs the Invasion NS 4-6
SSN1-53	Anne of Green Gables NS 7-8
SSB1-40	Apple Celebration Gr. 4-6
SSB1-04	Apple Mania Gr. 2-3
SSB1-38	Apples are the Greatest Gr. P-K
SSB1-59	Arctic Animals Gr. 4-6
SSN1-162	Arnold Lobel Author Study Gr. 2-3
SSPC-22	Australia B/W Pictures
SSA1-05	Australia Gr. 5-8
SSM1-03	Autumn in the Woodlot Gr. 2-3
SSM1-08	Autumn Wonders Gr. 1
SSN1-41	Baby Sister for Frances NS 1-3
SSPC-19	Back to School B/W Pictures
SSC1-33	Back to School Gr. 2-3
SSN1-224	Banner in the Sky NS 7-8
SSN1-36	Bargain for Frances NS 1-3
SSB1-82	Bats Gr. 4-6
SSN1-71	BB – Drug Free Zone NS Gr. 1-3
SSN1-88	BB – In the Freaky House NS 1-3
SSN1-78	BB – Media Madness NS 1-3
SSN1-69	BB – Wheelchair Commando NS 1-3
SSN1-119	Be a Perfect Person-3 Days NS 4-6
SSC1-15	Be My Valentine Gr. 1
SSD1-01	Be Safe Not Sorry Gr. P-1

Code #	Title and Grade
SSN1-09	Bear Tales Gr. 2-4
SSB1-28	Bears Gr. 4-6
SSN1-202	Bears in Literature Gr. 1-3
SSN1-40	Beatrix Potter Gr. 2-4
SSN1-129	Beatrix Potter: Activity Biography Gr. 2-4
SSB1-47	Beautiful Bugs Gr. 1
SSB1-21	Beavers Gr. 3-5
SSN1-257	Because of Winn-Dixie NS Gr. 4-6
SSR1-53	Beginning Manuscript Gr. Pk-2
SSR1-54	Beginning Cursive Gr. 2-4
SSR1-57	Beginning and Practice Manuscript Gr. PK-2
SSR1-58	Beginning and Practice Cursive Gr. 2-4
SSN1-33	Bedtime for Frances NS 1-3
SSN1-114	Best Christmas Pageant Ever NS Gr. 4-6
SSN1-32	Best Friends for Frances NS Gr. 1-3
SSB1-39	Best Friends Pets Gr. P-K
SSN1-185	BFG NS Gr. 4-6
SSJ1-61	Big Book of Canadian Celebrations Gr. 1-3
SSJ1-62	Big Book of Canadian Celebrations Gr. 4-6
SSN1-35	Birthday for Frances NS Gr. 1-3
SSN1-107	Borrowers NS Gr. 4-6
SSC1-16	Bouquet of Valentines Gr. 2
SSN1-29	Bread & Jam for Frances NS Gr. 1-3
SSN1-63	Bridge to Terabithia NS Gr. 4-6
SSY1-24	BTS Numeración Gr. 1-3
SSY1-25	BTS Adición Gr. 1-3
SSY1-26	BTS Sustracción Gr. 1-3
SSY1-27	BTS Fonética Gr. 1-3
SSY1-28	BTS Leer para Entender Gr. 1-3
SSY1-29	BTS Uso de las Mayúsculas y Reglas de Puntuación Gr. 1-3
SSY1-30	BTS Composición de Oraciones Gr. 1-3
SSY1-31	BTS Composici13n de Historias Gr. 1-3
SSN1-256	Bud, Not Buddy NS Gr. 4-6
SSB1-31	Bugs, Bugs & More Bugs Gr. 2-3
SSR1-07	Building Word Families L.V. Gr. 1-2
SSR1-05	Building Word Families S.V. Gr. 1-2
SSN1-204	Bunnicula NS Gr. 4-6
SSB1-80	Butterflies & Caterpillars Gr. 1-2
SSN1-164	Call It Courage NS Gr. 7-8
SSN1-67	Call of the Wild NS Gr. 7-8
SSJ1-41	Canada & It's Trading Partners 6-8
SSPC-28	Canada B/W Pictures
SSN1-173	Canada Geese Quilt NS Gr. 4-6
SSJ1-01	Canada Gr. 1
SSJ1-33	Canada's Capital Cities Gr. 4-6
SSJ1-43	Canada's Confederation Gr. 7-8
SSF1-04	Canada's First Nations Gr. 7-8
SSJ1-51	Canada's Landmarks Gr. 1-3
SSJ1-48	Canada's Landmarks Gr. 4-6
SSJ1-60	Canada's Links to the World Gr. 5-8
SSJ1-42	Canada's Traditions & Celeb. Gr. 1-3
SSB1-45	Canadian Animals Gr. 1-2
SSJ1-37	Canadian Arctic Inuit Gr. 2-3
SSJ1-53	Canadian Black History Gr. 4-8
SSJ1-57	Canadian Comprehension Gr. 1-2
SSJ1-58	Canadian Comprehension Gr. 3-4
SSJ1-59	Canadian Comprehension Gr. 5-6
SSJ1-46	Canadian Industries Gr. 4-6
SSK1-12	Canadian Problem Solving Gr. 4-6
SSJ1-38	Canadian Provinces & Terr. Gr. 4-6
SSY1-07	Capitalization & Punctuation Gr. 1-3
SSN1-198	Captain Courageous NS Gr. 7-8
SSK1-11	Cars Problem Solving Gr. 3-4
SSN1-154	Castle in the Attic NS Gr. 4-6
SSF1-31	Castles & Kings Gr. 4-6
SSN1-144	Cat Ate My Gymsuit NS Gr. 4-6
SSPC-38	Cats B/W Pictures
SSB1-50	Cats – Domestic & Wild Gr. 4-6
SSN1-34	Cats in Literature Gr. 3-6
SSN1-212	Cay NS Gr. 7-8
SSM1-09	Celebrate Autumn Gr. 4-6
SSC1-39	Celebrate Christmas Gr. 4-6
SSC1-31	Celebrate Easter Gr. 4-6
SSC1-23	Celebrate Shamrock Day Gr. 2
SSM1-11	Celebrate Spring Gr. 4-6
SSC1-13	Celebrate Thanksgiving R. 3-4
SSM1-06	Celebrate Winter Gr. 4-6
SSB1-107	Cells, Tissues & Organs Gr. 7-8
SSB1-101	Characteristics of Flight Gr. 4-6
SSN1-66	Charlie & Chocolate Factory NS Gr. 4-6
SSN1-23	Charlotte's Web NS Gr. 4-6
SSB1-37	Chicks N'Ducks Gr. 2-4

Code #	Title and Grade
SSA1-09	China Today Gr. 5-8
SSN1-70	Chocolate Fever NS Gr. 4-6
SSN1-241	Chocolate Touch NS Gr. 4-6
SSC1-38	Christmas Around the World Gr. 4-6
SSPC-42	Christmas B/W Pictures
SST1-08A	Christmas Gr. JK/SK
SST1-08B	Christmas Gr. 1
SST1-08C	Christmas Gr. 2-3
SSC1-04	Christmas Magic Gr. 1
SSC1-03	Christmas Tales Gr. 2-3
SSG1-06	Cinematography Gr. 5-8
SSPC-13	Circus B/W Pictures
SSF1-03	Circus Magic Gr. 3-4
SSJ1-52	Citizenship/Immigration Gr. 4-8
SSN1-104	Classical Poetry Gr. 7-12
SSN1-227	Color Gr. 1-3
SSN1-203	Colour Gr. 1-3
SSN1-135	Come Back Amelia Bedelia NS 1-3
SSH1-11	Community Helpers Gr. 1-3
SSK1-02	Concept Cards & Activities Gr. P-1
SSN1-183	Copper Sunrise NS Gr. 7-8
SSN1-86	Corduroy & Pocket Corduroy NS 1-3
SSN1-124	Could Dracula Live in Wood NS 4-6
SSN1-148	Cowboy's Don't Cry NS Gr. 7-8
SSR1-01	Creativity with Food Gr. 4-8
SSB1-34	Creatures of the Sea Gr. 2-4
SSN1-208	Curse of the Viking Grave NS 7-8
SSN1-134	Danny Champion of World NS 4-6
SSN1-98	Danny's Run NS Gr. 7-8
SSK1-21	Data Management Gr. 4-6
SSB1-53	Dealing with Dinosaurs Gr. 4-6
SSN1-178	Dear Mr. Henshaw NS Gr. 4-6
SSB1-22	Deer Gr. 3-5
SSPC-20	Desert B/W Pictures
SSJ1-40	Development of Western Canada 7-8
SSA1-16	Development of Manufacturing 7-9
SSN1-105	Dicken's Christmas NS Gr. 7-8
SSN1-62	Different Dragons NS Gr. 4-6
SSPC-21	Dinosaurs B/W Pictures
SSB1-16	Dinosaurs Gr. 1
SST1-02A	Dinosaurs Gr. JK/SK
SST1-02B	Dinosaurs Gr. 1
SST1-02 C	Dinosaurs Gr. 2-3
SSN1-175	Dinosaurs in Literature Gr. 1-3
SSJ1-26	Discover Nova Scotia Gr. 5-7
SSJ1-36	Discover Nunavut Territory Gr. 5-7
SSJ1-25	Discover Ontario Gr. 5-7
SSJ1-24	Discover PEI Gr. 5-7
SSJ1-22	Discover Québec Gr. 5-7
SSL1-01	Discovering the Library Gr. 2-3
SSB1-106	Diversity of Living Things Gr. 4-6
SSK1-27	Division Drills Gr. 4-6
SSB1-30	Dogs – Wild & Tame Gr. 4-6
SSPC-31	Dogs B/W Pictures
SSN1-196	Dog's Don't Tell Jokes NS Gr. 4-6
SSN1-182	Door in the Wall NS Gr. 4-6
SSB1-87	Down by the Sea Gr. 1-3
SSN1-189	Dr. Jeckyll & Mr. Hyde NS Gr. 4-6
SSG1-07	Dragon Trivia Gr. P-8
SSN1-102	Dragon's Egg NS Gr. 4-6
SSN1-16	Dragons in Literature Gr. 3-6
SSC1-06	Early Christmas Gr. 3-5
SSB1-109	Earth's Crust Gr. 6-8
SSC1-21	Easter Adventures Gr. 3-4
SSC1-17	Easter Delights Gr. P-K
SSC1-19	Easter Surprises Gr. 1
SSPC-12	Egypt B/W Pictures
SSN1-255	Egypt Game NS Gr. 4-6
SSF1-28	Egyptians Today & Yesterday Gr. 2-3
SSJ1-49	Elections in Canada Gr. 4-8
SSB1-108	Electricity Gr. 4-6
SSN1-02	Elves & the Shoemaker NS Gr. 1-3
SSH1-14	Emotions Gr. P-2
SSB1-85	Energy Gr. 4-6
SSN1-108	English Language Gr. 10-12
SSN1-156	Enjoying Eric Wilson Series Gr. 5-7
SSB1-64	Environment Gr. 4-6
SSR1-12	ESL Teaching Ideas Gr. K-8
SSN1-258	Esperanza Rising NS Gr. 4-6
SSR1-22	Exercises in Grammar Gr. 6
SSR1-23	Exercises in Grammar Gr. 7
SSR1-24	Exercises in Grammar Gr. 8
SSF1-20	Exploration Gr. 4-6
SSF1-15	Explorers & Mapmakers of Can. 7-8
SSJ1-54	Exploring Canada Gr. 1-3
SSJ1-56	Exploring Canada Gr. 1-6
SSJ1-55	Exploring Canada Gr. 4-6
SSH1-20	Exploring My School & Community 1
SSPC-39	Fables B/W Pictures
SSN1-15	Fables Gr. 4-6
SSN1-04	Fairy Tale Magic Gr. 3-5
SSPC-11	Fairy Tales B/W Pictures

Code #	Title and Grade
SSN1-11	Fairy Tales Gr. 1-2
SSN1-199	Family Under the Bridge NS Gr. 4-6
SSPC-41	Famous Canadians B/W Pictures
SSJ1-12	Famous Canadians Gr. 4-8
SSN1-210	Fantastic Mr. Fox NS Gr. 4-6
SSB1-36	Fantastic Plants Gr. 4-6
SSPC-04	Farm Animals B/W Pictures
SSB1-15	Farm Animals Gr. 1-2
SST1-03A	Farm Gr. JK/SK
SST1-03B	Farm Gr. 1
SST1-03C	Farm Gr. 2-3
SSJ1-05	Farming Community Gr. 3-4
SSB1-44	Farmyard Friends Gr. P-K
SSJ1-45	Fathers of Confederation Gr. 4-8
SSB1-19	Feathered Friends Gr. 4-6
SST1-05A	February Gr. JK/SK
SST1-05B	February Gr. 1
SST1-05C	February Gr. 2-3
SSN1-03	Festival of Fairytales Gr. 3-5
SSC1-36	Festivals Around the World Gr. 2-3
SSN1-168	First 100 Sight Words Gr. 1
SSC1-32	First Days at School Gr. 1
SSJ1-06	Fishing Community Gr. 3-4
SSN1-170	Flowers for Algernon NS Gr. 7-8
SSN1-261	Flat Stanley NS Gr. 1-3
SSN1-128	Fly Away Home NS Gr. 4-6
SSD1-05	Food: Fact, Fun & Fiction Gr. 1-3
SSD1-06	Food: Nutrition & Invention Gr. 4-6
SSB1-118	Force and Motion Gr. 1-3
SSB1-119	Force and Motion Gr. 4-6
SSB1-25	Foxes Gr. 3-5
SSN1-263	Fractured Fairy Tales NS Gr. 1-3
SSN1-172	Freckle Juice NS Gr. 1-3
SSB1-43	Friendly Frogs Gr. 1
SSN1-260	Frindle NS Gr. 4-6
SSB1-89	Fruits & Seeds Gr. 4-6
SSN1-137	Fudge-a-Mania NS Gr. 4-6
SSB1-14	Fun on the Farm Gr. 3-4
SSR1-49	Fun with Phonics Gr. 1-3
SSPC-06	Garden Flowers B/W Pictures
SSK1-03	Geometric Shapes Gr. 2-5
SSC1-18	Get the Rabbit Habit Gr. 1-2
SSN1-209	Giver, The NS Gr. 7-8
SSN1-190	Go Jump in the Pool NS Gr. 4-6
SSG1-03	Goal Setting Gr. 6-8
SSG1-08	Gr. 3 Test – Parent Guide
SSG1-99	Gr. 3 Test – Teacher Guide
SSG1-09	Gr. 6 Language Test–Parent Guide
SSG1-97	Gr. 6 Language Test–Teacher Guide
SSG1-10	Gr. 6 Math Test – Parent Guide
SSG1-96	Gr. 6 Math Test – Teacher Guide
SSG1-98	Gr. 6 Math/Lang. Test–Teacher Guide
SSK1-14	Graph for all Seasons Gr. 1-3
SSN1-117	Great Brain NS Gr. 4-6
SSN1-90	Great Expectations NS Gr. 7-8
SSN1-169	Great Gilly Hopkins NS Gr. 4-6
SSN1-197	Great Science Fair Disaster NS Gr. 4-6
SSN1-138	Greek Mythology Gr. 7-8
SSN1-113	Green Gables Detectives NS 4-6
SSC1-26	Groundhog Celebration Gr. 2
SSC1-25	Groundhog Day Gr. 1
SSB1-113	Growth & Change in Animals Gr. 2-3
SSB1-114	Growth & Change in Plants Gr. 2-3
SSB1-48	Guinea Pigs & Friends Gr. 3-5
SSB1-104	Habitats Gr. 4-6
SSPC-18	Halloween B/W Pictures
SST1-04A	Halloween Gr. JK/SK
SST1-04B	Halloween Gr. 1
SST1-04C	Halloween Gr. 2-3
SSC1-10	Halloween Gr. 4-6
SSC1-08	Halloween Happiness Gr. 1
SSC1-29	Halloween Spirits Gr. P-K
SSY1-13	Handwriting Manuscript Gr 1-3
SSY1-14	Handwriting Cursive Gr. 1-3
SSC1-42	Happy Valentines Day Gr. 3
SSN1-205	Harper Moon NS Gr. 7-8
SSN1-123	Harriet the Spy NS Gr. 4-6
SSC1-11	Harvest Time Wonders Gr. 1
SSN1-136	Hatchet NS Gr. 7-8
SSC1-09	Haunting Halloween Gr. 2-3
SSN1-91	Hawk & Stretch NS Gr. 4-6
SSC1-30	Hearts & Flowers Gr. P-K
SSN1-22	Heidi NS Gr. 4-6
SSN1-120	Help I'm Trapped in My NS Gr. 4-6
SSN1-24	Henry & the Clubhouse NS Gr. 4-6
SSN1-184	Hobbit NS Gr. 7-8
SSN1-122	Hoboken Chicken Emerg. NS 4-6
SSN1-250	Holes NS Gr. 4-6
SSN1-116	How Can a Frozen Detective NS 4-6
SSN1-89	How Can I be a Detective if I NS 4-6
SSN1-96	How Come the Best Clues... NS 4-6

Publication Listing

Code #	Title and Grade
SSN1-133	How To Eat Fried Worms NS Gr.4-6
SSR1-48	How To Give a Presentation Gr. 4-6
SSN1-125	How To Teach Writing Through 7-9
SSR1-10	How To Write a Composition 6-10
SSR1-09	How To Write a Paragraph 5-10
SSR1-08	How To Write an Essay Gr. 7-12
SSR1-03	How To Write Poetry & Stories 4-6
SSD1-07	Human Body Gr. 2-4
SSD1-02	Human Body Gr. 4-6
SSN1-25	I Want to Go Home NS Gr. 4-6
SSH1-06	I'm Important Gr. 2-3
SSH1-07	I'm Unique Gr. 4-6
SSF1-05	In Days of Yore Gr. 4-6
SSF1-06	In Pioneer Days Gr. 2-4
SSM1-10	In the Wintertime Gr. 2
SSB1-41	Incredible Dinosaurs Gr. P-1
SSN1-177	Incredible Journey NS Gr. 4-6
SSN1-100	Indian in the Cupboard NS Gr. 4-6
SSPC-05	Insects B/W Pictures
SSPC-10	Inuit B/W Pictures
SSJ1-10	Inuit Community Gr. 3-4
SSN1-85	Ira Sleeps Over NS Gr. 1-3
SSN1-93	Iron Man NS Gr. 4-6
SSN1-193	Island of the Blue Dolphins NS 4-6
SSB1-11	It's a Dogs World Gr. 2-3
SSM1-05	It's a Marshmallow World Gr. 3
SSK1-05	It's About Time Gr. 2-4
SSC1-41	It's Christmas Time Gr. 3
SSH1-04	It's Circus Time Gr. 1
SSC1-43	It's Groundhog Day Gr. 3
SSB1-75	It's Maple Syrup Time Gr. 2-4
SSC1-40	It's Trick or Treat Time Gr. 2
SSN1-65	James & The Giant Peach NS 4-6
SSN1-106	Jane Eyre NS Gr. 7-8
SSPC-25	Japan B/W Pictures
SSA1-06	Japan Gr. 5-8
SSN1-264	Journey to the Centre of the Earth NS Gr. 7-8
SSC1-05	Joy of Christmas Gr. 2
SSN1-161	Julie of the Wolves NS Gr. 7-8
SSB1-81	Jungles Gr. 2-3
SSE1-02	Junior Music for Fall Gr. 4-6
SSE1-05	Junior Music for Spring Gr. 4-6
SSE1-06	Junior Music for Winter Gr. 4-6
SSR1-62	Just for Boys - Reading Comprehension Gr. 3-6
SSR1-63	Just for Boys - Reading Comprehension Gr. 6-8
SSN1-151	Kate NS Gr. 4-6
SSN1-95	Kidnapped in the Yukon NS Gr. 4-6
SSN1-140	Kids at Bailey School Gr. 2-4
SSN1-176	King of the Wind NS Gr. 4-6
SSF1-29	Klondike Gold Rush Gr. 4-6
SSF1-33	Labour Movement in Canada Gr. 7-8
SSN1-152	Lamplighter NS Gr. 4-6
SSB1-98	Learning About Dinosaurs Gr. 3
SSN1-38	Learning About Giants Gr. 4-6
SSK1-22	Learning About Measurement Gr. 1-3
SSB1-46	Learning About Mice Gr. 3-5
SSK1-09	Learning About Money CDN Gr. 1-3
SSK1-19	Learning About Money USA Gr. 1-3
SSK1-23	Learning About Numbers Gr. 1-3
SSB1-69	Learning About Rocks & Soils Gr. 2-3
SSK1-08	Learning About Shapes Gr. 1-3
SSB1-100	Learning About Simple Machines 1-3
SSK1-04	Learning About the Calendar Gr. 2-3
SSK1-10	Learning About Time Gr. 1-3
SSH1-17	Learning About Transportation Gr. 1
SSB1-02	Leaves Gr. 2-3
SSN1-50	Legends Gr. 4-6
SSC1-27	Lest We Forget Gr. 4-6
SSJ1-13	Let's Look at Canada Gr. 4-6
SSJ1-16	Let's Visit Alberta Gr. 2-4
SSJ1-15	Let's Visit British Columbia Gr. 2-4
SSJ1-03	Let's Visit Canada Gr. 3
SSJ1-18	Let's Visit Manitoba Gr. 2-4
SSJ1-21	Let's Visit New Brunswick Gr. 2-4
SSJ1-27	Let's Visit NFLD & Labrador Gr. 2-4
SSJ1-30	Let's Visit North West Terr. Gr. 2-4
SSJ1-20	Let's Visit Nova Scotia Gr. 2-4
SSJ1-34	Let's Visit Nunavut Gr. 2-4
SSJ1-17	Let's Visit Ontario Gr. 2-4
SSQ1-08	Let's Visit Ottawa Big Book Pkg 1-3
SSJ1-19	Let's Visit PEI Gr. 2-4
SSJ1-31	Let's Visit Québec Gr. 2-4
SSJ1-14	Let's Visit Saskatchewan Gr. 2-4
SSJ1-28	Let's Visit Yukon Gr. 2-4
SSN1-130	Life & Adv. of Santa Claus NS 7-8
SSB1-10	Life in a Pond Gr. 3-4
SSF1-30	Life in the Middle Ages Gr. 7-8
SSB1-103	Light & Sound Gr. 4-6
SSN1-219	Light in the Forest NS Gr. 7-8
SSN1-121	Light on Hogback Hill NS Gr. 4-6
SSN1-46	Lion, Witch & the Wardrobe NS 4-6
SSR1-51	Literature Response Forms Gr. 1-3
SSR1-52	Literature Response Forms Gr. 4-6
SSN1-28	Little House Big Woods NS 4-6
SSN1-233	Little House on the Prairie NS 4-6
SSN1-111	Little Women NS Gr. 7-8
SSN1-115	Live from the Fifth Grade NS 4-6
SSN1-141	Look Through My Window NS 4-6
SSN1-112	Look! Visual Discrimination Gr. P-1
SSN1-61	Lost & Found NS Gr. 4-6
SSN1-109	Lost in the Barrens NS Gr. 7-8
SSJ1-08	Lumbering Community Gr. 3-4
SSN1-167	Magic School Bus Gr. 1-3
SSN1-247	Magic Treehouse Gr. 1-3
SSB1-78	Magnets Gr. 3-5
SSD1-03	Making Sense of Our Senses K-1
SSN1-146	Mama's Going to Buy You a NS 4-6
SSB1-94	Mammals Gr. 1
SSB1-95	Mammals Gr. 2
SSB1-96	Mammals Gr. 3
SSB1-97	Mammals Gr. 5-6
SSN1-160	Maniac Magee NS Gr. 4-6
SSA1-19	Mapping Activities & Outlines! 4-8
SSA1-17	Mapping Skills Gr. 1-3
SSA1-07	Mapping Skills Gr. 4-6
SST1-10A	March Gr. JK/SK
SST1-10B	March Gr. 1
SST1-10C	March Gr. 2-3
SSB1-57	Marvellous Marsupials Gr. 4-6
SSK1-01	Math Signs & Symbols Gr. 1-3
SSB1-116	Matter & Materials Gr. 1-3
SSB1-117	Matter & Materials Gr. 4-6
SSH1-03	Me, I'm Special! Gr. P-1
SSK1-16	Measurement Gr. 4-8
SSC1-02	Medieval Christmas Gr. 4-6
SSPC-09	Medieval Life B/W Pictures
SSC1-07	Merry Christmas Gr. P-K
SSK1-15	Metric Measurement Gr. 4-8
SSN1-13	Mice in Literature Gr. 3-5
SSB1-70	Microscopy Gr. 4-6
SSN1-180	Midnight Fox NS Gr. 4-6
SSN1-243	Midwife's Apprentice NS Gr. 4-6
SSJ1-07	Mining Community Gr. 3-4
SSK1-17	Money Talks – Cdn Gr. 3-6
SSK1-18	Money Talks – USA Gr. 3-6
SSB1-56	Monkeys & Apes Gr. 4-6
SSN1-43	Monkeys in Literature Gr. 2-4
SSN1-54	Monster Mania Gr. 4-6
SSN1-97	Mouse & the Motorcycle NS 4-6
SSN1-94	Mr. Poppers Penguins NS Gr. 4-6
SSN1-201	Mrs. Frisby & Rats NS Gr. 4-6
SSR1-13	Milti-Level Spelling Program Gr. 3-6
SSR1-26	Multi-Level Spelling USA Gr. 3-6
SSK1-31	Addition & Subtraction Drills 1-3
SSK1-32	Multiplication & Division Drills 4-6
SSK1-30	Multiplication Drills Gr. 4-6
SSA1-14	My Country! The USA! Gr. 2-4
SSN1-186	My Side of the Mountain NS 7-8
SSN1-58	Mysteries, Monsters & Magic Gr. 6-8
SSN1-37	Mystery at Blackrock Island NS 7-8
SSN1-80	Mystery House NS 4-6
SSN1-157	Nate the Great & Sticky Case NS 1-3
SSF1-23	Native People of North America 4-6
SSF1-25	New France Part 1 Gr. 7-8
SSF1-27	New France Part 2 Gr. 7-8
SSA1-10	New Zealand Gr. 4-8
SSN1-51	Newspapers Gr. 5-8
SSN1-47	No Word for Goodbye NS Gr. 7-8
SSPC-03	North American Animals B/W Pictures
SSF1-22	North American Natives Gr. 2-4
SSN1-75	Novel Ideas Gr. 4-6
SST1-06A	November JK/SK
SST1-06B	November Gr. 1
SST1-06C	November Gr. 2-3
SSN1-244	Number the Stars NS Gr. 4-6
SSY1-03	Numeration Gr. 1-3
SSPC-14	Nursery Rhymes B/W Pictures
SSN1-12	Nursery Rhymes Gr. P-1
SSN1-59	On the Banks of Plum Creek NS 4-6
SSN1-220	One in Middle Green Kangaroo NS 1-3
SSN1-145	One to Grow On NS Gr. 4-6
SSB1-27	Opossums Gr. 3-5
SSJ1-23	Ottawa Gr. 7-9
SSJ1-39	Our Canadian Governments Gr. 5-8
SSF1-14	Our Global Heritage Gr. 4-6
SSH1-12	Our Neighbourhoods Gr. 4-6
SSB1-72	Our Trash Gr. 2-3
SSB1-51	Our Universe Gr. 5-8
SSB1-86	Outer Space Gr. 1-2
SSA1-18	Outline Maps of the World Gr. 1-8
SSB1-67	Owls Gr. 4-6
SSN1-31	Owls in the Family NS Gr. 4-6
SSL1-02	Oxbridge Owl & The Library Gr. 4-6
SSB1-71	Pandas, Polar & Penguins Gr. 4-6
SSN1-52	Paperbag Princess NS Gr. 1-3
SSR1-11	Passion of Jesus: A Play Gr. 7-8
SSA1-12	Passport to Adventure Gr. 4-5
SSR1-06	Passport to Adventure Gr. 7-8
SSR1-04	Personal Spelling Dictionary Gr. 2-5
SSPC-29	Pets B/W Pictures
SSE1-03	Phantom of the Opera Gr. 7-9
SSN1-171	Phoebe Gilman Author Study Gr. 2-3
SSY1-06	Phonics Gr. 1-3
SSK1-33	Picture Math Book Gr. 1-3
SSN1-237	Pierre Berton Author Study Gr. 7-8
SSN1-179	Pigman NS Gr. 7-8
SSN1-48	Pigs in Literature Gr. 2-4
SSN1-99	Pinballs NS Gr. 4-6
SSN1-60	Pippi Longstocking NS Gr. 4-6
SSF1-12	Pirates Gr. 4-6
SSK1-13	Place Value Gr. 4-6
SSB1-77	Planets Gr. 3-6
SSR1-74	Poetry Prompts Gr. 1-3
SSR1-75	Poetry Prompts Gr. 4-6
SSB1-66	Popcorn Fun Gr. 2-3
SSB1-20	Porcupines Gr. 3-5
SSR1-55	Practice Manuscript Gr. Pk-2
SSR1-56	Practice Cursive Gr. 2-4
SSF1-24	Prehistoric Times Gr. 4-6
SSE1-01	Primary Music for Fall Gr. 1-3
SSE1-04	Primary Music for Spring Gr. 1-3
SSE1-07	Primary Music for Winter Gr. 1-3
SSJ1-47	Prime Ministers of Canada Gr. 4-8
SSN1-262	Prince Caspian NS Gr. 4-6
SSK1-20	Probability & Inheritance Gr. 7-10
SSN1-49	Question of Loyalty NS Gr. 7-8
SSN1-26	Rabbits in Literature Gr. 2-4
SSB1-17	Raccoons Gr. 3-5
SSN1-207	Radio Fifth Grade NS Gr. 4-6
SSB1-52	Rainbow of Colours Gr. 4-6
SSN1-144	Ramona Quimby Age 8 NS 4-6
SSJ1-09	Ranching Community Gr. 3-4
SSY1-08	Reading for Meaning Gr. 1-3
SSR1-76	Reading Logs Gr. K-1
SSR1-77	Reading Logs Gr. 2-3
SSN1-165	Reading Response Forms Gr. 1-3
SSN1-239	Reading Response Forms Gr. 4-6
SSN1-234	Reading with Arthur Gr. 1-3
SSN1-249	Reading with Canadian Authors 1-3
SSN1-200	Reading with Curious George Gr. 2-4
SSN1-230	Reading with Eric Carle Gr. 1-3
SSN1-251	Reading with Kenneth Oppel Gr. 4-6
SSN1-127	Reading with Mercer Mayer Gr. 1-2
SSN1-07	Reading with Motley Crew Gr. 2-3
SSN1-142	Reading with Robert Munsch 1-3
SSN1-06	Reading with the Super Sleuths 4-6
SSN1-08	Reading with the Ziggles Gr. 1
SST1-11A	Red Gr. JK/SK
SSN1-147	Refuge NS Gr. 7-8
SSC1-44	Remembrance Day Gr. 1-3
SSPC-23	Reptiles B/W Pictures
SSB1-42	Reptiles Gr. 4-6
SSN1-110	Return of the Indian NS Gr. 4-6
SSN1-225	River NS Gr. 7-8
SSE1-08	Robert Schuman, Composer Gr. 6-9
SSN1-83	Robot Alert NS Gr. 4-6
SSB1-65	Rocks & Minerals Gr. 4-6
SSN1-149	Romeo & Juliet NS Gr. 7-8
SSB1-88	Romping Reindeer Gr. K-3
SSN1-21	Rumplestiltskin NS Gr. 1-3
SSN1-153	Runaway Ralph NS Gr. 4-6
SSN1-103	Sadako & 1000 Paper Cranes NS 4-6
SSD1-04	Safety Gr. 2-4
SSN1-42	Sarah Plain & Tall NS Gr. 4-6
SSC1-34	School in September Gr. 4-6
SSPC-01	Sea Creatures B/W Pictures
SSB1-79	Sea Creatures Gr. 1-3
SSN1-64	Secret Garden NS Gr. 4-6
SSB1-90	Seeds & Weeds Gr. 2-3
SSY1-02	Sentence Writing Gr. 1-3
SST1-07A	September JK/SK
SST1-07B	September Gr. 1
SST1-07C	September Gr. 2-3
SSN1-30	Serendipity Series Gr. 3-5
SSC1-22	Shamrocks on Parade Gr. 1
SSC1-24	Shamrocks, Harps & Shillelaghs 3-4
SSR1-66	Shakespeare Shorts-Perf Arts Gr. 1-4
SSR1-67	Shakespeare Shorts-Perf Arts Gr. 4-6
SSR1-68	Shakespeare Shorts-Lang Arts Gr. 2-4
SSR1-69	Shakespeare Shorts-Lang Arts Gr. 4-6
SSB1-74	Sharks Gr. 4-6
SSN1-158	Shiloh NS Gr. 4-6
SSN1-84	Sideways Stories Wayside NS 4-6
SSN1-181	Sight Words Activities Gr. 1
SSB1-99	Simple Machines Gr. 4-6
SSN1-19	Sixth Grade Secrets 4-6
SSG1-04	Skill Building with Slates Gr. K-8
SSN1-118	Skinny Bones NS Gr. 4-6
SSB1-24	Skunks Gr. 3-5
SSN1-191	Sky is Falling NS Gr. 4-6
SSB1-83	Slugs & Snails Gr. 1-3
SSB1-55	Snakes Gr. 4-6
SST1-12A	Snow Gr. JK/SK
SST1-12B	Snow Gr. 1
SST1-12C	Snow Gr. 2-3
SSB1-76	Solar System Gr. 4-6
SSPC-44	South America B/W Pictures
SSA1-11	South America Gr. 4-6
SSB1-05	Space Gr. 2-3
SSR1-34	Spelling Blacklines Gr. 1
SSR1-35	Spelling Blacklines Gr. 2
SSR1-36	Spelling Blacklines Gr. 3
SSR1-37	Spelling Blacklines Gr. 4
SSR1-14	Spelling Gr. 1
SSR1-15	Spelling Gr. 2
SSR1-16	Spelling Gr. 3
SSR1-17	Spelling Gr. 4
SSR1-18	Spelling Gr. 5
SSR1-19	Spelling Gr. 6
SSR1-27	Spelling Worksavers #1 Gr. 3-5
SSM1-02	Spring Celebration Gr. 2-3
SST1-01A	Spring Gr. JK/SK
SST1-01B	Spring Gr. 1
SST1-01C	Spring Gr. 2-3
SSM1-01	Spring in the Garden Gr. 1-2
SSB1-26	Squirrels Gr. 3-5
SSB1-112	Stable Structures & Mechanisms 3
SSG1-05	Steps in the Research Process 5-8
SSG1-02	Stock Market Gr. 7-8
SSN1-139	Stone Fox NS Gr. 4-6
SSN1-214	Stone Orchard NS Gr. 7-8
SSN1-01	Story Book Land of Witches Gr. 2-3
SSR1-64	Story Starters Gr. 1-3
SSR1-65	Story Starters Gr. 4-6
SSR1-73	Story Starters Gr. 1-6
SSY1-09	Story Writing Gr. 1-3
SSB1-111	Structures, Mechanisms & Motion 2
SSN1-211	Stuart Little NS Gr. 4-6
SSK1-29	Subtraction Drills Gr. 1-3
SSY1-05	Subtraction Gr. 1-3
SSY1-11	Successful Language Pract. Gr. 1-3
SSY1-12	Successful Math Practice Gr. 1-3
SSW1-09	Summer Learning Gr. K-1
SSW1-10	Summer Learning Gr. 1-2
SSW1-11	Summer Learning Gr. 2-3
SSW1-12	Summer Learning Gr. 3-4
SSW1-13	Summer Learning Gr. 4-5
SSW1-14	Summer Learning Gr. 5-6
SSN1-159	Summer of the Swans NS Gr. 4-6
SSZ1-02	Summer Olympics Gr. 4-6
SSM1-07	Super Summer Gr. 1-2
SSN1-18	Superfudge NS Gr. 4-6
SSA1-08	Switzerland Gr. 4-6
SSN1-20	T.V. Kid NS. Gr. 4-6
SSA1-15	Take a Trip to Australia Gr. 2-3
SSB1-102	Taking Off With Flight Gr. 1-3
SSK1-34	Teaching Math with Everyday Munipulatives Gr. 4-6
SSN1-259	The Tale of Despereaux NS Gr. 4-6
SSN1-55	Tales of the Fourth Grade NS 4-6
SSN1-188	Taste of Blackberries NS Gr. 4-6
SSK1-07	Teaching Math Through Sports 6-9
SST1-09A	Thanksgiving JK/SK
SST1-09C	Thanksgiving Gr. 2-3
SSN1-77	There's a Boy in the Girls... NS 4-6
SSN1-143	This Can't Be Happening NS 4-6
SSN1-05	Three Billy Goats Gruff NS Gr. 1-3
SSN1-72	Ticket to Curlew NS Gr. 4-6
SSN1-82	Timothy of the Cay NS Gr. 7-8
SSF1-32	Titanic Gr. 4-6
SSN1-222	To Kill a Mockingbird NS Gr. 7-8
SSN1-195	Toilet Paper Tigers NS Gr. 4-6
SSJ1-35	Toronto Gr. 4-8
SSH1-02	Toy Shelf Gr. P-K
SSPC-24	Toys B/W Pictures
SSN1-163	Traditional Poetry Gr. 7-10
SSH1-13	Transportation Gr. 4-6
SSW1-01	Transportation Snip Art
SSB1-03	Trees Gr. 2-3
SSA1-01	Tropical Rainforest Gr. 4-6
SSN1-56	Trumpet of the Swan NS Gr. 4-6
SSN1-81	Tuck Everlasting NS Gr. 4-6
SSN1-126	Turtles in Literature Gr. 1-3
SSN1-45	Underground to Canada NS 4-6

Publication Listing

Code #	Title and Grade
SSN1-27	Unicorns in Literature Gr. 3-5
SSJ1-44	Upper & Lower Canada Gr. 7-8
SSN1-192	Using Novels Canadian North Gr. 7-8
SSC1-14	Valentines Day Gr. 5-8
SSPC-45	Vegetables B/W Pictures
SSY1-01	Very Hungry Caterpillar NS 30/Pkg Gr. 1-3
SSF1-13	Victorian Era Gr. 7-8
SSC1-35	Victorian Christmas Gr. 5-8
SSF1-17	Viking Age Gr. 4-6
SSN1-206	War with Grandpa SN Gr. 4-6
SSB1-91	Water Gr. 2-4
SSN1-166	Watership Down NS Gr. 7-8
SSH1-16	Ways We Travel Gr. P-K
SSN1-101	Wayside Sch. Little Stranger NS Gr. 4-6
SSN1-76	Wayside Sch. is Falling Down NS 4-6
SSB1-60	Weather Gr. 4-6
SSN1-17	Wee Folk in Literature Gr. 3-5
SSPC-08	Weeds B/W Pictures
SSQ1-04	Welcome Back – Big Book Pkg 1-3
SSB1-73	Whale Preservation Gr. 5-8
SSH1-08	What is a Community? Gr. 2-4
SSH1-01	What is a Family? Gr. 2-3
SSH1-09	What is a School? Gr. 1-2
SSJ1-32	What is Canada? Gr. P-K
SSN1-79	What is RAD? Read & Discover 2-4
SSB1-62	What is the Weather Today? Gr. 2-4
SSN1-194	What's a Daring Detective NS 4-6
SSH1-10	What's My Number Gr. P-K
SSR1-02	What's the Scoop on Words Gr. 4-6
SSN1-73	Where the Red Fern Grows NS Gr. 7-8
SSN1-87	Where the Wild Things Are NS Gr. 1-3
SSN1-187	Whipping Boy NS Gr. 4-6
SSN1-226	Who is Frances Rain? NS Gr. 4-6
SSN1-74	Who's Got Gertie & How...? NS Gr. 4-6
SSN1-131	Why did the Underwear ... NS 4-6
SSC1-28	Why Wear a Poppy? Gr. 2-3
SSJ1-11	Wild Animals of Canada Gr. 2-3
SSPC-07	Wild Flowers B/W Pictures
SSB1-18	Winter Birds Gr. 2-3
SSZ1-03	Winter Olympics Gr. 4-6
SSM1-04	Winter Wonderland Gr. 1
SSC1-01	Witches Gr. 3-4
SSN1-213	Wolf Island NS Gr. 1-3
SSE1-09	Wolfgang Amadeus Mozart 6-9
SSB1-23	Wolves Gr. 3-5
SSC1-20	Wonders of Easter Gr. 2
SSY1-15	Word Families Gr. 1-3
SSR1-59	Word Families 2,3 Letter Words Gr. 1-3
SSR1-60	Word Families 3, 4 Letter Words Gr. 1-3
SSR1-61	Word Families 2, 3, 4 Letter Words Big Book Gr. 1-3
SSB1-35	World of Horses Gr. 4-6
SSB1-13	World of Pets Gr. 2-3
SSF1-26	World War II Gr. 7-8
SSN1-221	Wrinkle in Time NS Gr. 7-8
SSPC-02	Zoo Animals B/W Pictures
SSB1-08	Zoo Animals Gr. 1-2
SSB1-09	Zoo Celebration Gr. 3-4

Code #	Title and Grade

Code #	Title and Grade

Code #	Title and Grade